INVENTORY 1985

INVENTORY 98

D1295479

The Songs of the Minnesingers

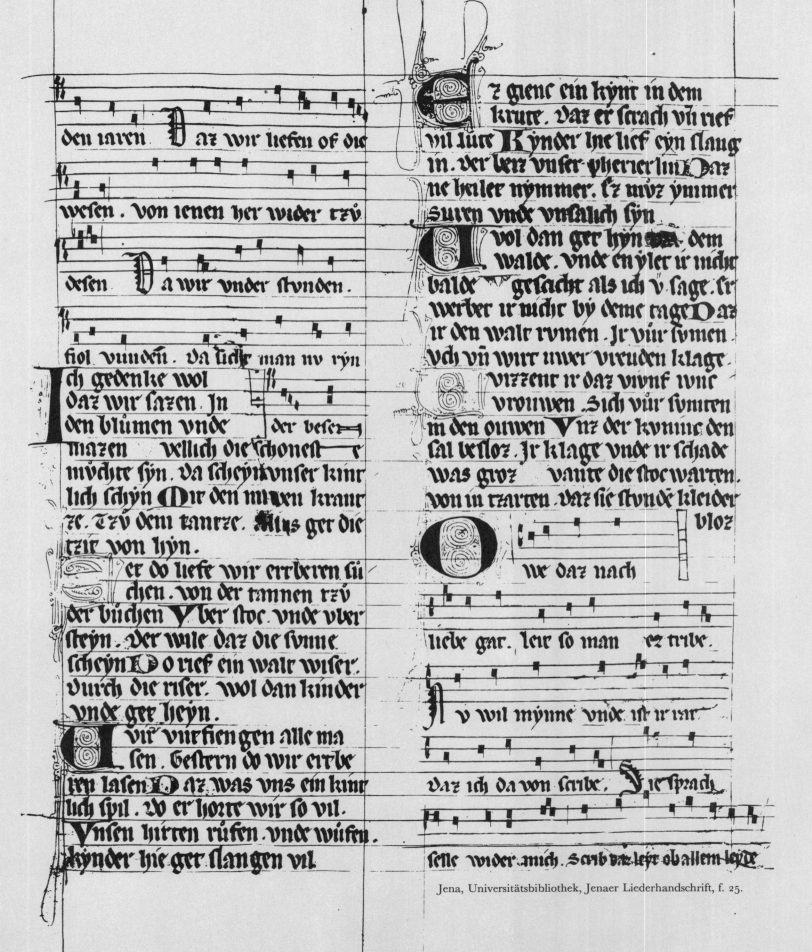

Jena, Universitätsbibliothek, Jenaer Liederhandschrift, f. 25.

The Songs
of the Minnesingers

Barbara Garvey Seagrave
and Wesley Thomas

University of Illinois Press · Urbana and London
1966

to

Lina, Gene, and Bruce,

in appreciation for their help and encouragement,
this work is affectionately dedicated.

Acknowledgment

During the preparation of this work we have become indebted to a number of individuals and institutions to which we would like to express our appreciation. For their assistance in obtaining primary and secondary source material we are grateful to Mrs. Harold Hantz, of the University of Arkansas Library; Father Kevin Watkins, O.S.B., of the New Subiaco Abbey; Oberbibliotheksrat Siegfried Joost, of the Heidelberg University Library; Dr. Hornung, of the Stiftung Preussischer Kulturbesitz; and Professor Dr. Hans-Joachim Lang and Mr. Klaus Popp, of the University of Tübingen. For permission to use copyrighted and otherwise restricted material we are indebted to Professor Dr. Friedrich Gennrich, Breitkopf & Härtel and Associated Music Publishers, The Harvard University Press, and the Stiftung Preussischer Kulturbesitz. For their valuable contributions to preparing the record we are grateful to the performers, Mr. Jerry Davidson, Mrs. Lester Howick, Professor Allan Gove, and Professor Roger Widder; to the sound engineer, Mr. Philip Eagle; and to Professor Lawrence Guinn, who instructed the vocalists in Middle High German diction. Finally, we should like to thank Dean Adkisson and the Graduate Council of the University of Arkansas for a generous research grant.

Table of Contents

The Songs of the Minnesingers

Introduction

The Development of a Secular Culture

The minnesong was one of the many products of the great cultural changes which western Europe underwent during the twelfth century. At this time two social classes, knights and townsmen, became large enough to rank near the clergy and the peasantry in numbers and importance; the courts of the higher nobility began to rival the monasteries as cultural centers; German, French, and Provençal began to rival Latin as written languages and vehicles for literature; and the Holy Roman Empire of the German Nation, which had declined greatly since the days of Charlemagne, once more became the dominant force in Europe, a force which gave it a measure of peace and stability. These developments and others combined to produce a much more secular culture than the previous centuries had known.

The most significant factors that contributed to the cultural changes of twelfth-century Germany were the First Crusade, which took place shortly before the century began, and the Second Crusade, which was carried out some fifty years later. These crusades brought German knights into contact with the cultures of Byzantium and the Near East, cultures which stressed the enjoyment of life and had produced the means whereby man's desire for beauty, comfort, and pleasure might be satisfied. The ever-increasing trade which followed the crusades brought to Germany not only the luxuries of the Orient—pottery, textiles, tapestries, rugs, dyes, and spices—but also, to a certain extent, the art and literature of the East. Trade increased also with Italy to the south, with France to the west, and even with the Moorish kingdom of Spain. Germany for the first time came into intimate contact with Mediterranean life and culture.

The most immediate social effect of the first two crusades was the growth of the centers of trade, the towns, and the emergence of the townspeople as an important social group. Of much greater significance, however, for the culture of the period was the increase in importance of the *Ministeriale,* usually referred to as the knights, who were the holders of the small feudal grants. It was to this group that the emperor Konrad III turned to build up his armies for the Second Crusade, and it was with the knights that the succeeding Hohenstaufen emperors allied themselves in their struggle to increase the authority of the Empire at the expense of the individual German princes. The greater military and political power which this alliance gave to the knights brought with it a heightened class-consciousness that soon developed its own unique and highly idealistic code of ethics and morality—chivalry.

Chivalry was not merely a secular doctrine to which one subscribed, but an all-embracing creed that determined the knight's varied activity and in which he was as carefully indoctrinated as was the priest in his theology. The chivalric training began at an early age. At about age seven the young aristocrat was sent away to another court to receive his education; if the father was influential, the boy might even be accepted at the court of the emperor. There, while serving as a page, he was taught to ride and use a sword and lance and was introduced to the rules of the court. At the age of fourteen or fifteen the youth became a squire, whose duty it was to attend the knight in battle or in tournaments, to care for his horse and weapons, and to act as his aid. When the squire reached his early twenties and was sufficiently versed in military skills and the meticulous social etiquette of the time, he was dubbed knight. But chivalry was more than a military and social code. Its chief goal was the achieving of a perfect balance between temporal and spiritual good, the combining of the enjoyment of earthly pleasures with the service of God. The ideal of the knight was a spiritual-physical harmony, a seriousness tempered with gaiety, a nobility joined to beauty. He strove for a union of the diverse elements of his heritage: the Germanic virtues of loyalty and bravery, the humanity and compassion of Christianity, and the Greek and Oriental delight in beauty, grace, form, and pageantry. This complete harmony finds expression in the mystic symbol of the

Holy Grail, which Wolfram's hero seeks in the courtly epic *Parzival*. It is also expressed in the glorification of *minne,* a highly formalized concept of love, and the idealization of woman.

The rise of the knightly class as a political and moral force was accompanied by an increase in the importance of knightly culture to the extent that it soon surpassed in significance the predominantly clerical culture which had prevailed in Germany since its Christianization. With the flowering of knightly culture the language of the knights, German, also began to come into its own. Although the earliest literary monuments in the German language date back to the eighth century, Latin remained the chief written language throughout the following centuries and, except for such Bible translations and commentaries, sermons, and other theological writings as the priests found useful in their ministry, little appeared in the vernacular. Since practically no one but the clergy knew Latin, the manuscripts of the period before the middle of the twelfth century were largely of an ecclesiastical nature, and such secular verses and tales as were composed remained largely unrecorded. To be sure, some secular literature appeared in Latin, and some works which were originally composed in German have survived in Latin versions. Nevertheless, the position of Latin as almost the sole written language and of the clergy as almost its only scribes delayed the development of a secular literature until well into the twelfth century. By then, however, many of the knights had learned to read and write or had begun to employ clerics as scribes and, inspired perhaps by the increased use of the vernacular in Provence, had begun to record their poetic productions in their native tongue. It was a fortunate coincidence that at the same time that the knightly class became the cultural leader in the West, the importation of the art of paper-making from the Orient provided a cheap means through which its literature might be preserved.

The first half of the twelfth century, which saw the development of a native literary language and of an art-conscious social class, was largely a period of preparation for the remarkable achievements of the next hundred years in architecture, painting, music, and literature. This century of cultural flowering coincides with the domination of Europe by the Swabian Hohenstaufens (1138–1250). The second of the Hohenstaufen emperors, Friedrich I (Barbarossa), was not only an astute military leader and politician, but also a patron of music and literature. In the series of rapid military campaigns which followed his coronation, Friedrich forced Denmark, Poland, and the cities of northern Italy to acknowledge the supremacy of the Empire and, through his marriage to Princess Beatrix of Burgundy, gained control of Lower Burgundy and Provence. The acquisition of Provence was of particular importance with regard to the cultural development of Germany, for it brought the Germans into closer contact with a land which had reacted more rapidly to the stimulation of the crusades than had the rest of Europe, a land where the secularization of culture was already well advanced.

Friedrich and his Hohenstaufen successors—his son, Heinrich VI, and his grandson, Friedrich II—enjoyed festivals, pageantry, and music; their courts became social centers for the German aristocracy and gathering places for the poets and musicians of Germany and Provence. It was there that the German pattern was set for the rituals of knighthood and the ideals of chivalry. These three Hohenstaufen emperors were closely identified with the social changes which determined the nature of the minnesong, and in the service of the Hohenstaufens the knightly class won its strength, splendor, and specific social morality. In contrast to the religious asceticism of former times there developed an open enjoyment of the pleasures of this world, a happy and festive affirmation of life, and an appreciation of beauty and sophisticated manners. There developed a love of well-ordered society with entertainments, ritualism, and fanciful conceits, a society in which social intercourse was refined to an aesthetic art. After the death of Friedrich II, the Empire became weak and the emperors ceased to exert an important influence on the cultural life of Germany. The specifically knightly culture also declined and soon lived only in the productions of poets and singers.

German Forerunners of the Minnesinger

The spiritual leader of the aristocratic society of the Hohenstaufen period, the priest of the cult of chivalry, was the minnesinger. He was the sophisticated descendant and heir of the old Germanic scop and the medieval *Spielmann* and *Vagant*. The scop was a warrior-musician of the Germanic tribes during the times of the great migrations of the fifth to the eighth century when the Germanic peoples spread over western Europe, northern Italy, Spain, and England. He inspired the warriors for battle with his songs of gods and heroes; he sang at the various heathen religious ceremonies; his music accompanied the great feasts in which the entire tribe participated; he performed at weddings, funerals, and on most other public or official occasions. However, since the scop was essentially a warrior and heathen priest, he disappeared with the end of the migrations and the Christianization of the Germanic tribes.

The successor to the scop was the professional entertainer known as the *Spielmann* (plural, *Spielleute*). He was a wanderer in a sense that the scop was not, for while the latter always remained with his tribe, the *Spielmann* was usually an itinerant without home or country. He was the professional distributor of news and literature at a time when there were no newspapers or books and few except the clergy could read. He transmitted orally everything from the heroic songs of the scops to long narrative poems, crude anecdotes, and the verse riddles which were so popular throughout the medieval period. As an actor of short mimic scenes he was for hundreds of years the only representative of secular drama in Germany. The public of the Middle Ages was dependent on the *Spielleute* for all of the stimulation that concert halls, theaters, bookstores, magazines, and newspapers bring to us. Moreover, all of the ruder forms of entertainment which modern society gets from circuses, night clubs, and county fairs were also supplied by the *Spielleute*. There were, of course, various types and classes of *Spielleute,* ranging from singers and musicians to acrobats and clowns.

The *Spielmann* singer, the direct descendant of the scop, was native to the German lands; the other *Spielleute* represented foreign traditions. Mimes, rope dancers, jugglers, acrobats, knife throwers, and sleight-of-hand artists had been popular with Roman audiences in the early days of the Roman Empire and, following its conquering armies, had become firmly established in the Gallic and British provinces. After the collapse of the Empire they began to penetrate also into Germany, where they provided entertainment for nobility and clergy as well as peasants and townspeople. They traveled about, singly and in groups, and managed to thrive in spite of the opposition of the Church and intermittent repression by the civil authorities. Alcuin, Augustine, and other churchmen denounced the *Spielleute;* Charlemagne forbade monasteries and cloisters to give them shelter or employment. In some places they had neither civil rights nor legal protection. Although widely condemned, they were nevertheless in demand for private and public festivities and sometimes even held permanent positions at one or another of the German courts. Such a court *Spielmann* had two chief duties: to provide entertainment for guests and, by means of eulogizing songs, to insure fame and immortality for his employer. Occasionally the court *Spielmann* received a fief of his own as a reward for his services and thereby entered the ranks of the minor aristocracy.

Many of the *Spielleute* were women—usually dancers, sometimes musicians. One English visitor to the court of Friedrich II tells of seeing Saracen girls, each standing on two rolling spheres which they guided with graceful movements about the room while clashing cymbals. Others played roles in the primitive and often obscene dramatic productions of the *Spielleute*. One woman, a talented singer by the name of Agnes, attained considerable power and importance as the mistress of King Wenzel II of Bohemia.

Although the *Spielleute* as a group were no more socially acceptable than are modern gypsies, they were of great importance to German culture. They kept alive some of the old heathen festivals, dances, and customs which the Church had banned; they preserved many of the songs of the scops about such early heroes as Siegfried, Hagen, Gunther, Attila, Dietrich of Bern, Walther of Acquitania, and others, thus providing the substance of German heroic literature; they carried stories, verses, and melodies from land to land, giving Germany the basis of a common cultural tradition. The *Spielmann* singer did not disappear with the advent of the minnesinger, but continued for centuries after the latter had vanished. During the time of the minnesingers the *Spielleute* collected and performed the compositions of their aristocratic colleagues and, through generations of oral transmission, so adapted them to the popular taste that they emerged in the fifteenth and sixteenth centuries as folk songs. Other folk songs, however, were the creations of the *Spielleute* themselves and witness to the exceptional talent of some of these unknown wanderers. A few of the *Spielleute* from the thirteenth century on could write, and these wrote down minnesong verses in little paper or parchment volumes as a part of their repertoires. Such notebooks were used by the collectors of the thirteenth, fourteenth, and fifteenth centuries in preparing the extant manuscripts of the songs of the minnesingers. The chief service which the *Spielleute* performed for the minnesingers, however, was to save their melodies for posterity by passing them down orally, in some cases for centuries, until some musician-monk or other collector could record them in a manuscript. Few, if any, of the minnesingers could read or write music, so had it not been for the *Spielleute,* all of the earlier and many of the later melodies would have been lost.

Since none of the *Spielmann* songs which were composed before the time of the minnesingers are extant, it is impossible to do more than guess as to the influence which the former may have exerted on the latter. While the *Spielmann* influence on the didactic verse of the minnesingers was probably significant, the influence on the verse of the courtly love songs of the early and the classical periods cannot have been very important, for these songs were the expression of a unique culture, one that existed only at the courts of the nobility and did not begin until the Hohenstaufen period. However, one can assume an increasing influence of *Spielmann* verse on that of the minnesingers after the classical period, especially on the dancing songs. It is possible that the nature scenes which appear in the minnesongs owe something to the *Spielmann,*

perhaps by way of the wandering clerics, the *Vaganten* (singular, *Vagant*). It also seems likely that the music of the minnesingers (as well as that of the Church) may have borrowed from the melodies of the *Spielleute,* for music is and has always been the most adaptable of the arts, moving easily back and forth between peasants and courtiers, between religious hymn and secular song. In addition to possible contributions to the verse and melodies of the minnesingers, the *Spielmann* provided them with a large public which was accustomed to musical entertainment and with the wealth of performance techniques in mime, dance, instrumental performance, and vocal style which results from a long performance tradition.

The third German predecessor of the minnesinger was the *Vagant,* who became important as a composer and entertainer about the beginning of the eleventh century. As a result of the rapid growth of the monastic schools, the clerical class became so large about this time that neither the Church nor the courts could assimilate it. The resulting unemployment was increased during the century by the reform movement which spread throughout Western Christendom from the monastery of Cluny. Discipline was tightened at the monasteries—the easy, self-indulgent life there disappeared. As a result, many monks left the monasteries. These runaway monks and unemployed clerics with now and then a disfrocked priest made up a new class of itinerant entertainers which supported itself by composing and singing songs, usually in Latin. Since Latin was still unchallenged as the literary language of Germany, there was a demand for the performances of the *Vaganten* at the monasteries, cloisters, and wherever else literate people assembled. For a time these wandering scholars were respected for their learning, talent, and cloth. Eventually, however, the vagrant life left its mark on their habits and characters. They became notorious for their drunkenness, profanity, and general depravity and were eventually considered to be no better than *Spielleute*. In 1259 they were strongly condemned by the synods of northern Germany; in 1287 they were deprived of their ecclesiastical privileges by the Council of Würzburg. It was not such actions by the Church which brought about their decline, however, but rather the gradual disappearance of an audience which could appreciate and would support entertainment in Latin. By the beginning of the fourteenth century the *Vaganten* were no longer a significant element in the development of verse and music in Germany.

In the early years the songs of the *Vaganten* were not appreciably different from other medieval Latin verse. They were learned, filled with classical references, particularly from Vergil, Horace, and Ovid, and directed exclusively to an educated and sophisticated audience. However, soon after the *Vaganten* were freed from the restraint of the Church and began to mingle with peasants and townspeople, a new life appeared in their scholarly productions. They learned the songs of the *Spielleute,* observed the popular dances and listened to the choral singing which accompanied them, celebrated the formerly pagan spring festivals with the peasants, and became acquainted with nature and elemental pleasures. The *Vaganten* wrote didactic verse, particularly satires against churchmen, Rome, and the Pope which doubtless influenced the didactic songs of the minnesingers, especially those of Walther von der Vogelweide. They also composed religious songs, which in those days commonly made up a part of each singer's repertoire. The *Vaganten* are primarily known, however, for their frankly sexual, often bawdy, love songs, to which they often adapted the melodies of hymns and sequences. In these songs they sang also of birds, flowers, forests, streams, zephyrs, and clouds, and popularized the identification of nature and love and the contrast between winter and love. In such verses can be seen the origin of the "nature introduction" of the minnesongs, although it is possible that either the *Spielmann* or the composers of certain Latin hymns or both may have been ultimately responsible for this poetic phenomenon. Another poetic device which was introduced into secular verse by the *Vaganten* was the refrain. This, too, later appeared in the minnesong.

Since the early songs of the *Spielleute* have not been preserved, those of the *Vaganten* are the first in Germany in which we find the spontaneous expression of sensual pleasure. This pleasure was usually erotic in nature and the songs boldly describe masculine desires and feminine acquiescence. Love was portrayed as purely sexual, and in language which was at the same time witty and frivolous and strong and vital. Allusions to antique mythology abound in these verses, especially to Cupid and Venus, and many erotic conceits of Ovid and other Roman poets can also be detected. Since the songs of the *Vaganten,* like those of the minnesingers, were sophisticated and varied in form and style, it is probable that the minnesong owes more to these secular Latin love songs than to the lost folk songs of the *Spielleute.*

Vaganten songs appeared in the Rhineland area about the beginning of the eleventh century and from there spread eastward through Germany. They appear to have been especially popular in southern Germany, particularly in Bavaria. The best known of the German *Vaganten* was a poet of considerable talent who called himself Archipoeta. He remained for some time at the court of Friedrich Barbarossa, where his performances were apparently very well received.

Only a little *Vaganten* music has survived, and unfortunately all of that is notated in staffless neumes (that is, notation which shows no definite pitch indications but only the shape and direction of the melodic elements). Only one song from the entire repertory can be assigned definite pitches. "O admirabile Veneris ydolum," written in staffless neumes in an eleventh-century manuscript (Cambridge, Univ. Lib. Gg. v, 35), also appears in two other manuscripts: one has both the *Vagant* text and that of a hymn, "O Roma nobilis" (Vatican, 3327), and the other contains only the hymn text with exact pitch notation (Monte Cassino, Q 318). It is not certain whether the hymn is a contrafact of the *Vagant* love song or whether the secular song may be a parody of the hymn.

The Verse of the Monasteries and Cloisters

From the time of the disintegration of the Roman Empire until the development of a culture-conscious secular society in the twelfth century, the clergy was almost the sole bearer of Western culture, and one must look to it for the literary sources of the songs of the minnesingers. The *Vaganten* songs, although stamped both by the wandering and dissolute life of their composers and by the influence of the folk songs of the *Spielleute,* belong essentially to the literary tradition of the monasteries and cloisters. Indeed, in the case of many compositions, one does not know whether the author was a monk or a *Vagant.* However, the *Vaganten* songs are hardly representative of clerical literature.

Since the minnesingers composed primarily love songs, the question naturally arises as to whether there was a tradition of erotic verse in the medieval Latin monastic writings from which the minnesingers could have drawn. Such a tradition did exist, although the nature and extent of the eroticism varied greatly. Poems and letters in verse exchanged between nuns and priests which reveal affection and sympathy date back as far as the sixth century. Most of these, of course, show a bond between the two which is more spiritual than physical. The word *amor* frequently appears, but it seems to indicate *amor spiritualis* rather than *amor carnalis.* Such correspondence was essentially an outgrowth of a common mission, a need for sympathetic friendship, and a desire for literary expression. Among others, St. Boniface, the Anglo-Saxon missionary to Germany, composed such letters to nuns.

That some compositions were not free of worldly elements is indicated, however, by a directive sent out by Charlemagne in 789 which forbade the nuns to write *winileodos.* These were social songs in German which presumably included love songs. A directive of the following century expressly forbids the nuns to compose or sing *puellarum cantica* (girls' songs). But the erotic content of medieval Latin literature did not become considerable or pronounced until the revival of interest in classical Roman literature which took place in the tenth and eleventh centuries. During this renaissance a considerable amount of secular literature appeared, written in Latin by priests, monks, and nuns. Hrothswith, a nun of the cloister at Gandersheim, composed the first dramas to be written in a German land, dramatic dialogues modeled after those of Terence, which, for all their moral intent, contained much of the Roman's eroticism. The monk Ekkehard of the St. Gall monastery composed his heroic poem *Waltharius,* which, though it is primarily an account of legendary Germanic warriors, also presents a love story and reveals the influence of Vergil. The unknown cleric who wrote the romance *Ruodlieb* described the colorful adventures and the loves of a wandering knight and included a song of the type later called *Liebesgruss* (love's greeting). Of special interest with regard to the minnesong are two epistles in verse which were preserved in the Tegernsee monastery. They both contain a *Frauenklage* (lady's plaint): her lover has been absent for a long time; she is fearful that he may not be faithful and is sad with pangs of love; since she has never done anything to justify being thus forsaken, her lover should return and still her pain. These letters, which show the influence of Cicero's *Laelius,* are remarkably similar in content to the lady's plaints of the early minnesong. Similar verse epistles were composed also by priests and nuns at Regensburg and elsewhere. One of the most famous medieval Latin manuscripts, the *Carmina Cantabrigiensa,* a twelfth-century copy of writings collected by a German cleric, contains a number of erotic poems, among them a *Frauenklage* and an amorous dialogue between a priest and a nun. In the latter selection can be traced the influence of Ovid's *Ars Amatoria,* a poem on the art of making love which enjoyed considerable popularity throughout the Middle Ages. The fictional love letters of Ovid's *Heroïdes* were also well known and frequently imitated.

One of the most important contributions which the monasteries and cloisters made to the development of the courtly love song of the minnesingers resulted from the cult of the Virgin Mary, which became particularly significant in the eleventh century. A host of songs, hymns, and sequences were composed in her praise; her virtues were extolled in an extravagant language which is not unlike that of love verse. Indeed, the high-born, lovely, but unapproachable heroine of many of the minnesongs owes a great deal to the medieval Latin concept of Mary. It is also possible that the poems dealing with the lament of Mary over the loss of her son may have contributed to the *Frauenklage* of the minnesingers. The best known of the songs in praise of Mary is perhaps the "Marienlied von Melk," an Austrian choral composition of the early twelfth century.

In addition to love songs, the monasteries and cloisters produced other types which were taken over and adapted by the minnesingers: didactic songs, religious songs, and crusade songs. There are fifteen of the latter still extant in medieval Latin, and it is more than probable that some of them were known to the eleven minnesingers who composed crusade songs.

Troubadours and Trouvères

The cultural revolution which produced the first courtly literature and music in Germany had taken place almost a century before in Provence. In the area of Poitou, Marche, and Limousin appeared the earliest secular songs in the vernacular; these were carried by the troubadours to France, England, northern Spain, Italy, and finally to Germany. Their art was from the very beginning highly sophisticated, both in concepts and in form. It developed from the same sources as those from which the minnesong sprang: folk songs, the songs of wandering clerics, and the verse and music of priests and nuns. It may also have been influenced by the songs of Moorish Spain. According to the so-called Arabo-Persian theory, the strophic structure, rhythms, melodies, and themes of the Provençal songs can be traced back to the Andalusian songs of the Caliphate of Cordova and from there to Persian ghasels and the Hellenistic songs of pre-Christian Alexandria. However, while it is true that many interesting parallels exist between Arabian-Persian songs and those of Provence and even between the chivalric cultures which both expressed, it is also true that the essential elements of Provençal song were present in the medieval Latin tradition of the West.

The earliest troubadour whose works have been preserved was William IX (1071–1127), Duke of Aquitaine and Count of Poitou. Like William, most troubadours were of noble rank; twenty-three were reigning princes. Originally they sang their own songs to their assembled courts, but later they employed itinerant musicians—jongleurs—to perform for them. The subjects of the troubadour songs were varied; they included love, religion, politics, famous people of the day, and subjects derived from nature, such as dawn and spring. Troubadour music gradually disappeared during the thirteenth century as a result of the destruction of Provence during the Albigensian Crusade.

In the meantime, the art of the troubadours had taken root and found a new direction in northern France. When Eleanor of Acquitaine, the granddaughter of the first troubadour, came to Paris about 1137 as the queen of Louis VII of France, she brought with her several troubadours. Their music and verse were well received at the French court and soon were imitated and adapted by the French trouvères, who, however, were known in Germany more for their narrative verse than for their lyric verse. The lyric forms they cultivated included many types of complicated refrain forms in which both musical and poetic repetitions were used with great ingenuity.[1] Forms of this type probably evolved originally out of dance forms.

The compositions of the troubadours and trouvères had no effect on the beginnings of the German minnesong, but they greatly influenced its development. Melodies, metrical patterns, and themes passed across the Rhine, together with an entire terminology of poetic expressions and many of the concepts and ideas of chivalry and courtly love. The classical minnesong represented the harmonious union of Romance and native German elements.

The Minnesingers

It is difficult to generalize about the life or position of a minnesinger, for this designation applied to all those who composed and sang songs dealing with courtly love, *minne*. Indeed, it may also include those who used the form and language of the minnesong to treat subjects other

[1]An example of the use of refrains in which the trouvères delighted may be found in the *virelai* form outlined below:

Music	AB	CC	AB	AB
Poetry	AB	CD	EF	AB
	refrain		musical refrain with new words	refrain

Although such sophisticated refrain forms had a great influence on later French music, their effect on the German minnesong was negligible.

than *minne*. The minnesingers came from many classes of society. Among those whose songs have been preserved was an emperor, the Hohenstaufen Heinrich VI; two kings, Konrad IV of Germany and Wenzel II of Bohemia; six other ruling princes, Prince Wizlaw III of Rügen, Duke Heinrich I of Anhalt, Duke Heinrich IV of Breslau, Duke Johann I of Brabant, Margrave Otto IV of Brandenburg, and Margrave Heinrich II of Meissen. There were some dozen counts, the most important of whom were Rudolf von Fenis and Hugo von Montfort, and about sixty nobles of the *Ministerial* class. From the middle of the thirteenth century on, the ranks of the minnesingers were swelled by about thirty middle-class singers and several clerics. The largest and most representative group was that of the minor nobility, but even within this group there were great variations with regard to wealth and position. Friedrich von Hausen was wealthy and a prominent man of his day; Walther von der Vogelweide was a penniless wanderer who was dependent on his songs for his livelihood. As the minnesong developed and then declined, the general trend with regard to rank and importance of its singers was steadily downward. The first generation of minnesingers all belonged to propertied nobility; the chief representatives of the second generation were impecunious nobility who had become professional entertainers; commoners appeared in the third generation, and their numbers gradually increased until at its end the minnesong was completely taken over by middle-class artisans, the meistersingers.

Most of the minnesingers of all ranks and stations traveled widely. Wars, crusades, politics, family affairs, tournaments, and festivals took the princes and wealthy nobility on many journeys; necessity and wanderlust drove the penniless from court to court. Thus the minnesongs and the reputations of their singers were spread throughout the German-speaking lands. The chief centers of the minnesongs were those courts where there was a great deal of social life and entertainment. Particularly renowned in this respect were those of the Swabian Hohenstaufens, the dukes of Babenberg in Vienna, Margrave Dietrich of Meissen, and, most famous and boisterous of all, that of Count Hermann of Thuringia.

At these courts and others a rather large, aristocratic leisure class which required a considerable amount of entertaining assembled for the first time in German history. There were hunts, tournaments, dances, evenings devoted to singing, and whole weeks taken up with the narration of one or another of the courtly epics of the day.

On a minnesong evening a group of knights and ladies would amuse themselves by performing their own compositions or listening to those of a professional composer and singer. The singer would sometimes accompany himself with a stringed instrument, and sometimes be accompanied by one or more other instrumentalists. We can assume that the minnesinger, like his plebian contemporary, the *Spielmann,* was an actor and mimic. His song was delivered with gestures, sighs, winks, dramatic facial expressions, and pauses and hesitations in delivery, all of which affected both verse and music. The fact that the minnesong was above all a performance, which the composer-singer may have varied from time to time and which subsequent performers may have altered frequently before either words or music were recorded, sometimes makes it impossible to ascertain definitely the intent of the composer. It may be that some of the songs which appear to be filled with pain and sorrow were sung with a knowing smile or in a comically exaggerated manner, so that what seems to be tragic is actually comic. It is at least certain that there was a considerable amount of intentional and witty ambiguity and playing with words in the minnesong, almost from its beginning. A part of the ambiguity of the minnesong lies in the awareness of both performer and audience that the world of which he sings is not that in which they live. Another ambiguity is implicit in the situation of a performer singing a song in which incidents are recounted in the first person. To what extent does the performer identify himself with the hero of the song? Does he sometimes shift his point of view from that of the hero to that of the narrator and back again? Only the actual performance, of which today we know nothing, could tell. In general one should assume in the case of the love song that the performer does not represent himself, but his audience; that the experience is not specifically his, but one in which all share. This assumption is particularly valid in the case of the penniless knight who, though rank and birth entitled him to mingle socially with his listeners, nevertheless remained something of an outsider.

The Cult of Minne

The most important aspect of the songs of the minnesingers was the cult of *minne* and the idealization of woman. An exact definition of *minne* is not possible, for the hundred or more minnesingers who used the term frequently disagreed on its meaning and sometimes there was little consistency in its employment throughout the works of a single composer. The general conception of *minne* is that of an erotic passion which is both physical and spiritual, but which reaches no fulfillment. Although the concept did not appear in the earliest minnesongs, but entered later by way of France, it received almost immediate acceptance in Germany, for it filled a literary and aesthetic need and could be supported by tradition. *Minne* is on the one hand a secularization of the adoration of the Virgin Mary, in that the knight fixes his affections on a high-born lady who, like the Virgin, must be worshiped from afar. On the other hand it is a refinement and sublimation of the drives and virtues of ancient pagan times. The chief virtues of the Germanic heroes were *stæte* and *triuwe*. Where the Germanic hero showed his constancy (*stæte*) by enduring untold hardships in difficult campaigns and his loyalty (*triuwe*) by dying in battle to defend and support his leader, the medieval knight could demonstrate the same characteristics, and less painfully, in a social situation. The minnesinger speaks not merely for himself but for all knights when he sings of the pains of love. He emphasizes his ability (and theirs) to endure suffering by portraying his passion and frustration as limitless. (The fact that the lady can withstand such fervor only points up the greatness of her virtue.) He demonstrates his (and their) unswerving loyalty by insisting that, although the lady does not in the least reward his affection, he will remain faithful to her forever. The lady in the minnesong is not portrayed as an individual, but is sketched only in the broadest terms, her chief characteristics being haughtiness, beauty, and desirability. However, the song is actually less about her than about *minne* itself and is less a praise of love than an exaltation of self, a demonstration of nobility in suffering.

There is a general assumption, which is not definitely confirmed by either the lyric or the narrative literature of the period, that the heroine of the minnesong was a married lady. The advantages of choosing the wife of another as the object of the minnesong are obvious. Her position offers a sufficient reason for the lack of success of the lover's suit; it can add a little spice of naughtiness to the song; and it enables the minnesinger to pretend that the object of his affections is among his listeners, the female portion of which consisted almost exclusively of married women. However, the fact that the object of the lover's desires is married is never expressly stated, nor is it really necessary to the song to assume that she is so. She, and with her all courtly ladies, is raised to an ideal of perfection of charm and beauty for which one longs intensely and unceasingly and, since no great ideal is ever attained in actuality, it is logically and aesthetically inevitable that she cannot be won.

It is quite likely that the concept of *minne* had little effect on the actual lives and actions of the knights and ladies of the court. But, at least on the level of social entertainment and make-believe, it became a significant moral and ethical force which no knight or lady might ignore. The cult of *minne* as revealed in the minnesong developed a specialized terminology in which words and expression had, in addition to their ordinary, everyday meanings, also courtly, erotic significances. A language for devotees came into being in which feudal terms were used to form a vocabulary of courtship.

It is the duty of the knight to serve his lady in every way, but in actuality this service consists in singing her praises and declaring his devotion. However, she must remain anonymous. No name, family, residence, or specific characteristics may be mentioned. Her identity must remain a secret because of the jealous rivals, of the spies who would destroy the reputations of the lady and her lover, of the guardians whose duty it is to keep them apart. These are the enemies of lovers who must be outwitted. They are indistinct, nebulous figures who are no more than symbols of the difficulties which stand in the way of true love; they are literary conventions which can be traced back to Ovid.

Although the minnesong was in general a song of longing and unsatisfied desires, there was a type of minnesong, the *Tagelied* or dawn song, in which love finds consummation. However, the emphasis is rarely on the joys of love, but rather on the sorrows of parting. For the night of love has passed and the ardent lover must now tear himself away from the weeping lady before their rendezvous is discovered. Once more nobility of character is demonstrated by depth of pain and sadness. This aspect of the minnesong is, of course, by no means curious, for many of the best love songs of all peoples and ages have dealt with longing and sorrow rather than with happiness. In this respect the minnesong reveals its universality, not its uniqueness.

In the later works of Walther von der Vogelweide and in those of his successors, another type of minnesong appears in which the formalized concepts of *minne* are absent. These songs, though composed in a sophisticated style and for a courtly audience, have as their heroines peasant girls who love and are loved in a simple and natural manner. However, the courtly love song did not disappear entirely, and the cult of *minne* was observed— at least as a tradition and literary pretense—by even the very last of the minnesingers. One may seek the origins of this Venus worship in either classical and Oriental culture or in the Christian tradition. Actually, one finds in the cult of *minne* both pagan-physical and Christian-spiritual elements, existing in a harmonious unity. *Minne* was the essence of beauty, of nobility, of devotion; and in the service of *minne* the courtly society could demonstrate all of the subtle manners, aesthetic sensibility, and controlled emotion of their sophisticated culture. This peculiar type of love and the terminology and ritual which accompanied it were essentially Romance rather than German and first appeared in the songs of the minnesingers as a result of the influence of troubadours and trouvères. The earliest of the German singers portray love as a quite natural and simple emotion.

The Types of Songs

The compositions of the minnesingers can be grouped into three categories: the minnesong, the *Spruch,* and the *Leich.* The earliest extant minnesongs consist of a single stanza of two rhymed couplets. Each line has six accented syllables, a varying number of unaccented syllables, and is divided in the middle by a caesura. Appearing almost at the same time, however, was a somewhat more complicated form in which the single stanza had a tripartite structure. There were an *Aufgesang* (rising song), made up of two *Stollen,* and an *Abgesang* (falling song). The two *Stollen,* which are metrically and musically identical, usually consist of four lines each in which the scene or situation of the song is described. The *Abgesang,* which is usually longer than a single *Stollen* but not so long as the *Aufgesang,* describes the resolution of the situation. The lines are either long with a caesura or short. The rhyme scheme shows couplets or alternating rhyme.

The musical form used for the tripartite minnesong is known as the *Barform* and is similar to the troubadour *canzo* and the trouvère *ballade* (A A B). In the *Barform* the two *Stollen* have the same melody and new material is used for the *Abgesang.* Often all or part of the melody of the *Stollen* reappears as the last part of the *Abgesang.* In the later minnesong, the *Stollen* melody is often quite long, and the *Abgesang* has only a very short section of new material before the return of the long *Stollen* melody (see p. 147).

The advent of the Romance influence greatly affected the form of the minnesong, making it much more complex, introducing lines of varying length and intricate rhyme pattern. The songs began to be polystrophic with each stanza having the same structure and melody. However, the minnesongs seldom achieved the total unity which modern songs usually have, for there was seldom a basic relationship between the stanzas. As a result, it is often impossible to tell what the proper sequence of the stanzas should be or even whether the stanzas represent a single poem or several. The modern hymn often presents a similar situation. The individual stanzas of the polystrophic song may or may not consist of *Aufgesang* and *Abgesang.*

Some minnesong texts have survived which use a simple refrain at the conclusion of each stanza, but no music has survived for refrain songs in the minnesong repertory.

Certain of the minnesongs are given specific designations based on their content, the most common being: *Frauenstrophe, Wechsel, Liebesgruss, Tagelied,* and *Kreuzlied.* The *Frauenstrophe* (woman's strophe) appears particularly and almost exclusively in the earliest period of the minnesong. It is a monologue by a woman in which she bewails the absence or neglect of her lover. The *Wechsel* (alternating song) presents a dialogue between two lovers. Sometimes they are in each other's presence; sometimes they convey their words by a messenger. The *Wechsel* is often combined with the *Tagelied.* The *Liebesgruss* (love's greeting) is a salutation, usually by a man, in which he praises his sweetheart and declares his love. The *Tagelied* (dawn song) describes the sadness of two lovers as they part at dawn. It is usually in the form of a dialogue. The *Kreuzlied* (crusade song) sometimes, but not always, contains a love motif and describes the sorrows of parting as well as the solemn dedication to a religious duty. Several of the crusade songs were composed to be sung in chorus by the crusaders.

The *Spruch* is a song, usually in one stanza, that treats subjects other than love. Its structure does not differ basically from that of the minnesong. The three most common topics which the *Spruch* presents are matters of a didactic or religious nature, the personal experiences of the singer, and political situations and events. The didactic *Sprüche* may relate moral stories or proverbs, discuss virtues and vices, or treat the relationship of man to God. Of greater importance to the history of the minnesingers are the *Sprüche* which deal with their personal experiences, for it is from them that we have, in the case of most of the minnesingers, our only knowledge concerning their lives, residences, and positions. Indeed, we would not even know the names of some of the minnesingers if it were not for such *Sprüche.* The political *Sprüche* are also important in this respect, for they enable us to establish approximate dates for the lives and compositions of their composers.

Although many of the knights composed *Sprüche,* they were more popular with bourgeois composers who, for their part, were generally less interested than the knights in the minnesong. Therefore, the relative number of the *Sprüche* increased rapidly during the thirteenth and fourteenth centuries, as the proportion of bourgeois composers increased. During this period the distinctions between the minnesong and the *Spruch* became less pronounced, and the two forms tended to merge. Some polystrophic *Sprüche* appeared, but it is difficult, much more so than with the minnesong, to determine in every case whether the composers intended stanzas having identical structures and melodies as components of a single song. The basic question is, did the minnesinger sing all such stanzas at one time and in a particular sequence? The general assumption in this anthology will be that the *Spruch* stanza is a complete song.

The longest lyric form used by the minnesingers is the *Leich,* derived from the Romance *lai.* It had a variable structure related both to the Latin sequence and to dances grouped in a series of parts like the *estampie.* The Romance forms consisted of a large number of stanzas whose construction varied in meter, rhyme scheme, line length, and stanza length. In musical structure, the stanzas often repeat the same music, frequently with different endings for the same tune. In the German *Leich,* as in the sequence, these repetitions generally occur twice (double versicles), although instances of three or four repetitions, of through-composed stanzas with no melodic repetition, and of repetitions of melodic material from earlier stanzas occur freely.

The most famous German *Leich* is Frauenlob's *Marienleich,* in which the double-versicle structure is strictly observed: for the forty-four sections of the poem, there are twenty-two different melodies. In the manuscript the words of the repeat are even written directly under the words of the first half of the stanza, so there is no variation at all of the repeated sections (see p. 186).

A much freer treatment of the musical structure is found in the portion included in the anthology of Alexander's *Leich* in which repetitions are sometimes varied, through-composed sections appear, and musical material from earlier stanzas is repeated with more or less variation (see p. 139).

The poetic material of the *Leich* includes either religious and meditative themes (related to the sequence) or secular forms and themes which suggest that the form was often a series of different dances.

The melody of the minnesong, *Spruch,* or *Leich* together with its specific metrical structure makes up its *Ton,* although the word is sometimes used to indicate the metrical structure alone. The minnesingers were very proud of the number of different *Töne* which they could devise, and they produced a great variety. Walther von der Vogelweide composed about one hundred melodies and metrical patterns, and other minnesingers were nearly as inventive. To use someone else's *Ton* was highly unethical and caused the offender to be branded as a *Ton* thief. The general tendency throughout the history of the minnesingers was toward increased complexity of *Ton* to the extent that many of the later songs are little more than pretentious displays of metrical ingenuity.

Despite this great pride in the use of original *Töne,* the minnesingers did use borrowed tunes from other sources as well as inventing their own. Many of the early minnesongs were actually new German texts, fitted to the older tunes of troubadours and trouvères, and preserving the poetic structure of the Romance originals. The extent to which the tunes were transformed or adapted in the process is a matter for conjecture, since only the texts of these songs are preserved in the German sources. Tunes to which new texts have been set are known as *contrafacts,* and modern scholars have been able to identify a number of tunes in French and Provençal collections which will fit specific minnesongs from the early period. It is impossible to be certain, however, which of the many versions of some of the French originals were the ones with which the Germans were acquainted, whether the versions of songs as they were known to the Germans were in sources now lost, whether they knew them from written sources or through oral tradition, or whether they deliberately changed them in some details for their own purposes when they borrowed them.

The process of using borrowed tunes continued through the history of the minnesong, for even Wizlaw, one of the last of the minnesingers, mentions setting words to a pre-existent tune which may have been his teacher's. The later minnesong, however, usually borrows from Germanic rather than Romance sources. The meistersingers, in turn, borrowed and adapted many tunes and structures of the minnesingers.

Dances and Dancing Songs

Toward the end of the classical period of the minnesong, there appeared a type of song—the courtly village song—which was obviously a dancing song. About the same time, the first *Leiche* were composed which can be readily identified as *Tanzleiche* (dance lays). These forms, particularly the former, became very popular and continued to be written throughout the subsequent history of the minnesong. It should not be assumed, however, that the courtly village songs and the *Tanzleiche* were the first courtly songs which accompanied dancing. Indeed, it may be that many of the earlier minnesongs were sung during dances. This is especially likely in the case of the songs which treat the seasons of the year, for dancing and singing were essential elements of the traditional folk festivals in which the different seasons were celebrated. The songs which mention dancing make a distinction between the slow and measured *hovetanz* (courtly dance) and the lively village dances which, at least by the end of the classical period, were also popular at the courts.

The oldest of the village dances was the *reie,* a choral dance performed in a line or circle and using both gliding and leaping movements. This type of dance is very ancient and was accompanied by singing. The singing was led by one person (*vorsinger*) who may also have performed the function of demonstrating to the dancers what was to follow (*vortanzer*). It is not clear whether these two terms imply two different persons or one leader who fulfilled both functions. The leader was often a young girl. The *reie* was a summer dance which was always performed in the open air and often alternated with a *tanz* (danced by couples or groups of three dancers). The *tanz* was also danced indoors in the winter season. It was accompanied by instrumental music, although on occasion it was also sung. The most famous text for an instrumental dance tune was the troubadour song "Kalenda maya," improvised by Raimbaut de Vaqueyras to the tune of an *estampie* which had just been played by the vielle players.

Within these general types, many different dances were included. There are several descriptions of a dance in which a boy or knight dances between two fair maidens, the *ridewanz* (see p. 113). The *hoppaldei* was a rough peasant dance in which the dancers shook their heads and shoulders violently and rapidly. Also mentioned in the poems were the *rotruwange* (apparently a German version of the trouvère *rotruenge,* a refrain form of dance), the *trei* (a dance performed by twelve couples), and the *stampenîe* (the Romance *estampie*). For further discussion of the form of the *estampie* see p. 142.

When the dances were performed in the villages, all the participants probably joined in the singing except the instrumentalists (though those not playing wind instruments might have sung also). The dancing and singing were led by soloists. One of Neidhart's songs ("Sinc an, guldîn huon," p. 113) suggests that villagers took turns as *vorsinger.* In court, however, the minnesinger himself was the soloist. A few refrain songs have survived in which the dancers or the courtiers joined in the refrain, although unfortunately the music for all the German refrain songs has perished. In other poetic types the minnesinger is still referred to as having the role of the *vorsinger,* and probably sang a stanza to be repeated (with or without words) by the dancers, then a second stanza while the dancers waited to repeat it, and so on to the end of the song (see p. 107).

One of the most striking features of medieval German dancers often remarked upon by foreigners was the importance of hand movements. They are mentioned as late as the sixteenth century and are clearly shown in the pictures of the Manesse manuscript. These hand movements are shown as highly stylized gestures which illustrated and heightened the meaning of the song being performed, and which were used as specific symbols in pictorial art even when dancing was not directly involved.

It is interesting to note that Hindu and other Far Eastern dancing is also characterized by ritual hand movement which has both narrative and religious meaning. The similarity of many of the Eastern gestures to the German

medieval hand signs may point to a pre-Christian origin, although the dance movements may have been brought to Europe by *Spielleute,* gypsies, or other wanderers. The possibility of gypsy influence is particularly intriguing, since the gypsies originated in India and were in the Near East Balkan area by the time of the crusades. Thus the crusaders might have brought back these Oriental gestures to the German area.

The connection between song and dance in Germany had, of course, existed in pre-Christian times and had been maintained by the *Spielleute.* Just as the old dance came into the courtly society (the *hovetanz* itself was probably a highly refined form of an older dance rather than a new invention by the court), so the minnesingers introduced the poetic dance traditions into the newly established court culture. It is possible that the rhythms for the dance songs which they composed were determined by those of the traditional dances.

The favored instruments for dancing, especially indoors, were those preferred for the minnesong in general, the *fidel* and the *gîge,* to which percussion instruments were probably added. All sorts of other instruments were combined for large festive occasions; and trumpets, pipes, shawms, horns, chalumeaux, triangles, and bagpipes are all mentioned or shown with dancers. When large groups of loud instruments were used, it is likely that the dances were not sung.

Transmission and Embellishment of the Songs

The factual history of the minnesongs begins not with their composition, but with the extant collections which were compiled from the end of the thirteenth to the middle of the fifteenth century. Therefore, the manner in which words and melodies were transmitted through one hundred to two hundred years is and must remain a matter of speculation. It is probable that most, if not all, of the minnesingers whose works appear in extant manuscripts could write words, but it is equally probable that few, if indeed any, of them could write music. There were, of course, music scribes available in some of the courts and it is more than likely that there were minnesong collections prepared which antedate those which were preserved. However, such manuscripts could not have been available to many of the hundreds of singers throughout Germany and Austria who were constantly performing the works of the better-known minnesingers. Even the meistersingers of the sixteenth century were apparently unaware of the existence of such now famous collections as those in the Manesse and Jena manuscripts. It must be assumed that many, perhaps most, of the older minnesongs were preserved and transmitted by an oral tradition during at least some of the many years before they were recorded in extant manuscripts. One may speculate that the little notebooks which the *Spielleute* carried for remembering the verses of their repertoire may have included some formulas written in staffless neumes, like the few remaining *Vaganten* melodies, but when the collections of poems such as the Manesse manuscript were made, any musical signs of the *Spielleute* were either considered unimportant or meaningless and were not preserved.

The method used for the transmission of the songs seems to have been the learning of a basic repertoire by rote. There is every reason to believe that the singer felt free to embellish and change the songs he learned according to his own expressive style and taste. Faint traces of the ornamentation have survived in those songs which finally were written down, after transmission in this manner for several generations. One of these is in the many little melismas which fall into fairly well-defined formulas and must have been intended to be performed in an ornamental style of which the rhythm indicated in modern transcriptions can only be an approximation.[2]

Unfortunately very few of the melodies have been preserved in more than one manuscript, so that comparison of the different versions of the same melody is seldom possible.[3] There is, however, another source of comparison of variant forms in the repeated *Stollen* of the *Barform*, which often make many small melodic changes in the repetition, mostly by the addition of passing tones or other ornamental figures to the repeated section. Slight as many of these modifications are, they indicate that the scribe wrote down just what the singer sang at that particular time, and suggest that usually some changes were made in

the repetitions of earlier sections, in an improvisatory manner. Though many of the songs were recorded with literal repeats, this does not preclude the possibility that some ornamentation was expected to be provided by the singer, and that he was free to improvise these in a new manner each time he sang the song.

More direct evidence of the kinds of embellishments used by the performer is found in the preludes and interludes in the Montfort manuscript (see pp. 202–12). These textless sections may have been vocal or instrumental in performance, although it seems reasonable to believe that the ones which appear before new phrases are instrumental. In many of these songs there are decorated versions of the line which follows in a less ornamented form for the singer (see p. 202). These are of special interest since the manuscript dates from the period of the composition of the songs and may have been prepared under the direction of the composer (Burk Mangolt) and the poet. Therefore, material which was usually improvised by an instrumentalist may have been prescribed by the composer, or at least the manner of the improvisation suggested by him.

Range and Mode of the Melodies

The range of the song melodies seldom exceeds an octave, and lies within a comfortable tenor range. The songs could also have been sung by women; and, although the extent of the participation of aristocratic women in singing in court is not known, it is clear that the dance songs in the villages were often sung by the village girls, and women singers were found among the *Spielleute*.

[2]See, for example, the song of Der Unverzagte, "Junger man von tzwenzich iaren," p. 156. Anglès suggests that for such melismatic songs, nonmensural notation and the inconsistent use of mensural signs throughout Europe indicate rhythmic execution which the scribes had no means of representing. See p. 19 for further discussion of this problem.

[3]A song and *Leich* by Alexander and one song by Neidhart are among the most important of these in the earlier minnesongs. Among the late minnesingers Oswald von Wolkenstein and the Monk of Salzburg have several songs which are found in more than one manuscript. For a discussion of the comparison of Alexander's song in its two versions, see Heinrich Husmann, "Minnesong," *Die Musik in Geschichte und Gegenwart,* IX (Kassel, Bärenreiter, 1961), 358.

Despite the wide variety of instruments of the period, few are depicted in the illustrations of the manuscripts which would have had a range lower than the tenor.

The songs use the scales of the church modes, as is also true of the other secular and sacred music of the time. Certain modes tend to be favored, however, particularly Dorian and Lydian,[4] and a considerable number use Ionian (the modern major scale) and Aeolian (the modern minor scale). The only accidental found in the minnesong repertory is the *b*-flat, which, when used with the Lydian mode, actually changes the scale to major. Some accidentals were intended to be added by the performer even though they were not written (*musica ficta*), usually to avoid the interval of the augmented fourth. The attitude toward the application of the modes to secular song was apparently very lax: Johannes de Grocheo says that one does not speak of the modes with reference to *musica vulgaris* (secular song), and Anonymous II considers trouvère songs examples of music in which *musica ficta* was to be used simply for the sake of melodic beauty, which would of course change the actual structure of the modes being used.[5] The method of oral transmission of the songs apparently led to changes in the mode used as the song was handed down, as shown in various versions of Gace Brulé's "De bone amor et de loiaul amie." See p. 58 for a comparison of two of the versions of this song, which may have served as the melody for a contrafact by Rudolf von Fenis.[6]

Minnesong Rhythm

The rhythmic performance of the songs of the minnesingers presents many problems, since the notation in which almost all of them are written indicates only the pitch and not the rhythm in which they are to be performed. To make the problem more frustrating, there are few references to the manner of performing secular music in the writings of medieval theorists, and the scattered remarks which apply to rhythm are ambiguous.[7] Therefore, most theories of minnesong rhythm assume that the basis for the rhythmic organization of the music must be sought in the texts.

Middle High German poetry is measured by the number of stressed syllables in the line. Most lines are constructed of two-syllable feet, with occasional dactyls resulting from the free addition of unaccented syllables to the line. The use of an unaccented syllable to begin the line is haphazard, and may not follow in all stanzas of the poem, so the presence or absence of an up-beat does not seem to affect the basic rhythmic structure. If the stressed syllables are indicated in the rhythm of the music only by accent, the accented and unaccented parts of the poetic foot would be equal in length.[8] This would produce

[4]The Dorian scale corresponds to the modern white-key scale, from *d* to *d*, with half-steps between the second and third and sixth and seventh degrees of the scale. The other authentic modes used in the minnesong are: Phrygian (*e* to *e*, with half-steps between the first and second and the fifth and sixth degrees), Lydian (*f* to *f*, with a half-step between the fourth and fifth degrees), Mixolydian (*g* to *g*, with half-steps between the third and fourth and the sixth and seventh degrees, rarely used in the minnesong), and the more modern scales, Ionian and Aeolian.

[5]Ernst Rohloff, *Der Musiktraktat des Johannes Grocheo*, Media Latinitas, II (Leipzig, Kommissionsverlag Gebrüder Reinecke, 1943). The treatise ascribed to Anonymous II is printed in Charles Coussemaker, *Scriptorum de musica medii aevi nova series*, I (Paris, Durand, 1864–76, reprint, 1931), 303.

[6]"De bone amour et de loiaul amie" was evidently a very well-known tune in its day, since it appears in various versions in no less than eleven different manuscripts with this text, and in two others with trouvère contrafact texts. It is impossible to say which of these many versions was known to Rudolf von Fenis. The two versions in this anthology are chosen to show a comparison between variant versions of a tune from this early period, and to give an opportunity for the comparison of the two texts which are so similar in poetic structure. It should be noted, however, that Fenis might have based his adaptation on another version, perhaps even one now lost, and that he may even have been familiar with a trouvère contrafact text as well as, or instead of, the original text given here.

[7]Most of these remarks occur in the treatise by Johannes de Grocheo (c. 1300), which has been reprinted by Johannes Wolf in *Sammelbände der internationalen Musikgesellschaft*, I (1899–1900), 69–130. A more recent modern edition of this treatise is that of Rohloff, *Der Musiktraktat des Johannes Grocheo*.

[8]This is the basis of the method used by Johannes Wolf, *Handbuch der Notationskunde*, I (Leipzig, Breitkopf & Härtel, 1913), 172 ff. Other early scholars such as Saran, Liliencron, and Riemann used the stress principle as the basis for their varied rhythmic interpretations of the songs. Riemann's application of the theory was of particular interest at the end of the nineteenth century, although it is not now accepted. His transcriptions use binary rhythms freely, combined with a principle he termed *Vierhebigkeit*, the organization of music into four-stress lines, through which he fitted the minnesongs into various structural molds. See Hugo Riemann, "Die Musik der deutschen Minnesinger," *Musikalisches Wochenblatt*, XXVIII-XXXVIII (1897–1907) and "Die Beck-Aubry'sche 'modale Interpretation' der Troubadourmelodien," *Sammelbände der internationalen Musikgesellschaft*, XI (1910), 569.

a duple meter with even note values occasionally sub-divided when an extra unaccented syllable appears in a foot or when an ornamental group of notes is used on one syllable.

Another theory holds that the stressed and unstressed parts of the foot are unequal in length, and that the stressed syllable is also a long syllable. This theory has been applied to German minnesongs by scholars who believe there is a strong connection between the rhythm of troubadour and trouvère music and that of minnesong, and who accept the view of Aubry[9] and Beck[10] that the scansion of Romance poetry into trochaic, iambic, or dactylic feet makes possible the use of the rhythmic modes of polyphonic music of the thirteenth century to produce the following rhythms in the monophonic repertory:

First Mode
(trochaic) $\frac{3}{4}$ ♩ ♪

Second Mode
(iambic) $\frac{3}{4}$ ♪ ♩

Third Mode
(dactylic) $\frac{6}{4}$ ♩. ♪ ♩

A further problem arises concerning the interpretation of the short syllables of the dactylic mode. It is argued that the inequality of these syllables was the result of the use of this rhythm in polyphonic compositions where it was necessary to fit it with other triple modes appearing in other voices. In monophonic music, where no such necessity exists, some scholars consider a binary interpretation of the rhythm possible, using the pattern $\frac{4}{4}$ ♩ ♪ ♪ .[11] Gennrich and others, however, have continued to use the triple interpretation of the dactylic mode for monophonic music in the belief that the concept of triple time was so basic for the polyphonic music of that time that it may be assumed to have had an all-pervading influence on music not written in mensural notation. Consequently they have used triple meter as the basis for all transcriptions of music based on the rhythmic modes.[12]

The relevance of a theory of rhythmic performance originally postulated for the music of the troubadours and the trouvères to the music of the minnesong is based on the strong Romance influence on the group of minne-singers including Friedrich von Hausen and Rudolf von Fenis in the late twelfth century. Many of their poems are modeled on French or Provençal originals, and will fit the melodies of their models. As has been discussed earlier, the use of borrowed melodies with new texts (contrafacts) was common in medieval song. The poets themselves speak of the practice of writing poems to pre-existing tunes. Research by such modern scholars as Frank and Gennrich has traced several such melodies which will fit both Romance and German texts. Some of the German texts are almost translations of Romance originals, although most imitate only the form and meter of the model.[13] Gennrich and others believe that the rhythmic performance of the melody was also carried over from one culture to the other, and so base the transcription of minnesong on the rhyth-mic modes.[14]

If the modal interpretation of minnesong is used, much of the preserved repertory will be in the first mode, with

[9]Pierre Aubry, "L'oeuvre mélodique des troubadours et des trouvères," *La revue musicale,* VII (1907), 317, 347, 389.

[10]Johann Baptist Beck, "Die modale Interpretation der mittelalterlichen Melodien," *Caecilia* (Strassburg), XXIV (1907), 97. This theory is also dis-cussed in Beck, *Die Melodien der Troubadours* (Strassburg, Truebner, 1908). He changed his views to allow some interpretation in duple meter in his 1927 edition of *Le chansonnier Cangé* (Philadelphia, University of Pennsylvania Press, 1927). The German scholar Friedrich Ludwig also adopted the modal principle for the transcription of medieval monody. See his "Zur 'modalen Interpretation' von Melodien des 12. und 13. Jahrhunderts," *Zeitschrift der internationalen Musikgesellschaft,* XI (1910), 379.

[11]Carl Parrish, *The Notation of Medieval Music* (New York, Norton, 1959), p. 51. Beck also used this interpretation in *Le chansonnier Cangé,* II, no. 99.

[12]Friedrich Gennrich, *Mittelhochdeutsche Liedkunst* (Darmstadt, Gennrich, 1954) and numerous other works.

[13]Gennrich, "Liedkontrafactur in mhd. und ahd. Zeit," *Zeitschrift für deutsches Altertum,* LXXXII (1948), 105–41; Gennrich, "Sieben Melodien zu mittelhochdeutschen Minneliedern," *Zeitschrift für Musikwissenschaft,* VII (1924–25), 65–98; István Frank and Wendelin Müller-Blatteau, *Trouvères und Minnesänger,* Vols. I and II (West-Ost-Verlag, Saarbrücken, 1952, 1956).

[14]Handschin and Anglès, although using the modal theory in their tran-scriptions of medieval monody, advocated a freer use of the modal patterns. Handschin feels that they are not always applicable, while Anglès has found evidence in Spanish mensurally notated sources of the use of binary rhythms and combinations of modal rhythmic patterns. For a fuller description of Anglès' theories, see p. 19. For Handschin's views see Jacques Handschin, "Die Modaltheorie und Carl Appels Ausgabe der Gesaenge von Bernart de Ventadorn," *Medium Aevum,* IV (1935), 69, and numerous other works.

many phrases beginning with up-beats (see p. 129).

In a few cases the predominance of ornamental patterns on the weak syllable of the foot suggests the use of the short-long pattern of the second mode within the measure, with the stressed syllable as the short note. One of Gennrich's transcriptions of Walther's crusade song uses this rhythm (see p. 90). Some of Hermann Damen's songs will fit this mode very well (see p. 164), but it seldom can be applied to most of the minnesong repertory.

Almost all the dactylic songs for which melodies can be provided are actually contrafacts of French melodies and come from the period of strong French influence. (See Hartmann's "Ich muoz von rehte den tac iemer minnen," p. 66, for a transcription in triple meter, and Walther's "Uns hat der winter geschat über al," p. 82, for a transcription in duple meter.)

A few songs exist in which the notation does not use rhythmically noncommittal neumes, but clearly mensural characters which show the rhythms of the modes. Most of these are in French manuscripts and are the tunes for contrafacts. Among these is the song previously mentioned (see p. 18) which Rudolf von Fenis may have used for a contrafact. This is found in several manuscripts and a lucky chance has preserved it in two different kinds of notation, nonmensural and mensurally notated in dactylic mode (see p. 58). Whether these different versions indicate different methods of performance or merely that the scribe of the nonmensural versions took for granted that the performer would use the proper rhythm for singing the song is a matter for conjecture. The existence of such mensurally notated songs in French and Provençal sources has been a strong argument in favor of a similar interpretation of other songs. Anglès has pointed out, however, that mensural notation appears only in songs in syllabic style in medieval monody. Melismatic songs do not seem to use mensural signs which are reliable or consistent, probably indicating that for this type of song the scribe had no means of representing the rhythmic execution by notational means.[15]

The Spanish manuscripts of the thirteenth century also contain some songs in mensural notation, and in the Escurial manuscript of the *Cantigas de Santa Maria* Anglès finds what he considers the most perfectly notated mensural manuscript of monodic music of the thirteenth century. In the *cantigas* of this manuscript he finds great rhythmic richness which can be interpreted and transcribed without reference to any theories outside the notation of the manuscript itself. The patterns used include triple modal rhythms, mixed modal rhythms (combinations of the rhythmic patterns of more than one rhythmic mode), duple rhythms, and even mixtures of triple and duple time in the same songs.[16] He believes that a similar rich variety of rhythms was used by other European singers, but was not preserved because the scribes lacked the notational skill possessed by the Spanish scribes. He points to connections between German and Spanish courts of the thirteenth century and to the presence of German musicians among the foreigners in the Alphonsine musical establishment to suggest the probability of wide dissemination of the traditions represented in the Spanish *cantigas*.[17] However, he points out that these immensely varied patterns are not dependent upon the poetic texts nor in any way determined by them, so that there is at the moment no way of establishing the reasons for the choice of musical rhythms, and therefore no way of producing a definitive rhythmic transcription employing them in the absence of mensural indications in the manuscript.[18]

Among the minnesong manuscripts there is only one song which uses any mensural indications before the very late period of the art. This is a song added to the Berlin manuscript of Neidhart von Reuenthal by a second scribe after the rest of the collection had been completed (see p. 108). In this song, stems are used for unaccented syllables which are to be sung as short notes. Since this song

[15]Higini Anglès, "Der Rhythmus der monodischen Lyrik des Mittelalters und seine Probleme," *Kongressbericht,* Internationale Gesellschaft für Musikwissenschaft, Vierter Kongress, Basle (1949), p. 45.

[16]Anglès, *La Música de las Cantigas de Santa María del Rey Alfonso el Sabio* (Diputación Provincial de Barcelona—Biblioteca Central, Barcelona, 1943), p. 98.

[17]Anglès, "Musikalische Beziehungen zwischen Deutschland und Spanien in der Zeit vom 5. bis 14. Jahrhundert," *Archiv für Musikwissenschaft,* XVI (1959), 11–18.

[18]Anglès, *Música de las Cantigas de Santa María,* p. 99.

is not stylistically different from any of the other songs of Neidhart, there is no reason to believe that the difference in notation indicates a difference in performance, especially since the strongly marked rhythms of his poetry all lend themselves well to this rhythmic interpretation.

In some of the later sources, such as the songs of Hugo von Montfort and the Monk of Salzburg, signs are used which could be interpreted as having a mensural meaning. In Montfort's manuscript stems are sometimes added to notes, but there seems to be no logical or consistent pattern in their use (see p. 210). Sometimes they seem to indicate the highest note of a phrase; in some songs they are used for every note of some phrases; occasionally they appear to lengthen a note. Montfort's manuscript also uses doubled notes occasionally to show long notes, and the same device is used by the Monk of Salzburg (see p. 199).

The very late monophonic songs of Oswald von Wolkenstein use mensural notation in some manuscripts, nonmensural notation in others, and a mixture in still others. All his polyphonic songs use the standard mensural notation of the period.

The existence of these traces of rhythmic signs in the late minnesong manuscripts is of very little value for determining the rhythm of the earlier music, but rather makes more puzzling the persistence of such an ambiguous form of notation at a time when clear and unambiguous forms of notation were available to the scribes writing the melodies. This suggests another possibility—that is, that some type of free rhythm was used by the singers which could not be notated by the collectors. This is the position taken by Curt Sachs, who feels that "the use of a rhythmically noncommittal notation in times when a metrical script was available indicates a free or optional rhythm."[19]

It is also possible that it points to the use of rhythmic conventions of performance, which, while strictly observed by the oral tradition through which they were handed down, could not be represented by any of the signs available, though they were neither free nor optional in the rendition of the song. The recovery of such performance conventions which could only have been learned from the singers themselves is, unfortunately, beyond the realm of possibility.

Discouraging as this situation is, however, experiments with various types of free rhythmic treatment yield interesting and musically satisfying results in many of the songs. The method used for transcribing some of the songs in this anthology to indicate a free rhythmic performance has been to make each separate note a quarter note and each ligature a group of eighth notes to be sung with rhythmic freedom, dwelling on particularly expressive notes or on the ends of phrases. Groups of shorter note values are almost always ornamental in character.

One of the few contemporary descriptions of minnesinger performance is contained in an interesting remark by Ulrich von Lichtenstein in his *Frauendienst*. He states that "high notes" (*noten ho*) and also "quick notes" (*snellen noten*) won him special praise, indicating the possibility of dwelling on high notes and singing ornamental groups of notes as faster passages. He also makes the puzzling remark that the fiddlers especially thanked him for his high notes. Perhaps this was merely the admiration of fellow musicians for the quality of his voice, but perhaps also the lengthening of these high notes gave them the opportunity to add embellishments of their own at the same time.

Even if the stress theory or the modal theory is adopted for the transcription of minnesong rhythm, it is well to remember that although the pitch was written down, the rhythm of minnesong always remained an oral tradition, even at the end of the period, when scanty reminders of what might have been special rhythmic effects are found in occasional manuscripts. As such, it is probable that not one, but several, conventions of performance were used in the course of the transmission of the melodies. If unequal note values, such as those of the modal theory, were used, the best approximation of them in modern notation is probably ♩ ♪, but the actual performance may well have been more or less unequal than this precise notation indicates. Similarly, if the transcription is based on the principle of equal values for stressed and unstressed notes,

[19]Curt Sachs, *Rhythm and Tempo* (New York, Norton, 1953), p. 178.

the actual performance might have been slightly un-equal—just as, in the Baroque era and in the popular music of our own day, even an apparently precise notation of rhythm may actually require slight alterations of the written values to conform to the performance traditions of the time. Westrup, pointing out that Johannes de Grocheo's treatise speaks of music which is not precisely measured ("non . . . praecise mensurata"), suggests that a regular rhythmic basis does not preclude considerable freedom on the part of the performer in solo song, and that this may be a clue to the performance of medieval monody.[20]

In this anthology, examples of all of these approaches to the solution of the problem of minnesong rhythm have been included with some explanation of the theory used in each particular case. None should be regarded, how-ever, as an exclusive solution to the rhythmic possibilities of the piece, but as a basis on which the singer may allow his own taste and sensitivity to guide him in discovering a satisfying method of performance of the music.

The Use of Instruments

Since the surviving manuscripts show only the line to be sung by the voice, the role of instruments in accom-panying vocal performances is a matter of conjecture. The literary, pictorial, and theoretic sources all agree in placing great emphasis on the use of musical instruments to ac-company singers and probably also to provide instrumen-tal preludes, interludes, and postludes to the songs. The only minnesinger manuscripts which contain much actual music which could have been used for instrumental interludes are the late manuscripts of Hugo von Montfort and the Monk of Salzburg. It is, however, quite possible that this sort of music would have been improvised by the instrumentalists throughout the earlier period of the art.

If the instruments were played at the same time the singer was singing, as well as providing interludes, they may have been played in unison with the singer, may have doubled the vocal line with embellishments of their own, or may have provided some form of primitive

harmony, since drone instruments like the bagpipe were among those used. One song of the Monk of Salzburg provides a part for the *pommer* (a low-pitched instrument of the double-reed family) which might have been similar to what instrumentalists had been improvising for earlier music.

The theorists and poets make clear that the favored instruments were the bowed stringed instruments. Two words are found in Middle High German for this type of instrument: *gîge* and *fidel*. These were actually two dif-ferent instruments, each of which existed in several sizes. The *gîge* had a pear-shaped body, flat top, and short neck, and was known elsewhere in Europe as the rebec. The *fidel* had an oval body with a slight narrowing at the waist of the instrument (the Romance term for this instrument is *vielle*). Both were played with a rounded bow and held against the chest while being played rather than under the chin as modern violins are. Thus it would be possible for the player to sing as he played, although it is impos-sible to be sure from the pictorial evidence whether this was the case. Johannes de Grocheo says that the player should be able to play any type of song on his instrument and indicates that he might add a postlude to the song.

A wide variety of other instruments, including harps, lutes, recorders, shawms (a double-reed ancestor of the oboe), small bagpipes, and percussion instruments such as small drums and timbrels (an instrument somewhat similar to the modern tambourine) might also have been used to accompany the minnesingers. For singing and dancing in the open, louder instruments such as bagpipes, horns, and trumpets were used. One of the Monk of Salzburg's songs calls specifically for a trumpet, but this was an exceptional case for performance of the minnesong (see p. 197).

The most famous picture showing minnesinger per-formance is of Frauenlob playing a *fidel,* while clustered around him listening are musicians holding a drum, recorder, shawm, small bagpipe, and small *fidel*. It is

[20]J. A. Westrup, "Medieval Song," *The New Oxford History of Music,* Vol. II: *Early Medieval Music up to 1300* (London, Oxford University Press, 1954), p. 227.

interesting to note that none of the figures are pictured as singing, nor are they playing together; perhaps this was the *fidel*-player's postlude to which Johannes de Grocheo referred.

The pictures and literary sources indicate that sometimes several instruments played together with the singer (usually instruments of contrasting tone colors, rather than several of one family), that sometimes he was accompanied by a single player or accompanied himself, and that the singer and the instruments sometimes alternated in performance. In the Frauenlob picture, some of the surrounding musicians are in dance postures, and at least one may be clapping his hands, suggesting that clapping and stamping sounds were used for percussive effects.

The Manuscripts

It can be assumed that by far the greater part of the courtly songs which were composed and performed during the period from the second half of the twelfth century to the middle of the fifteenth century has been lost. Many of them, no doubt, were never written down and existed only in an oral tradition; others, though recorded by the author, by a *Spielmann,* or by a cleric, fell victim to one or another of the countless great and small wars, fires, and other catastrophes with which Germany has been plagued; still others became so changed in the process of repeated oral transmission that they are no longer recognizable as minnesongs. The greatest losses, unfortunately, occurred among the earlier songs, those which from the standpoint of both verse and music are the most interesting. In some cases songs have survived, but the names of their composers have not; in other instances the names of the composers are known to us, but all of their songs have been lost. Many minnesingers who had large repertoires are represented today by only one or two stanzas; and even some of the most famous, such as Heinrich von Morungen, have suffered severe losses. The loss of melodies has, of course, been far greater than that of lyrics, for while most of the minnesingers could record their verses, very few of them were able to write down their

melodies. As a result, almost none of the twelfth-century melodies have been preserved, and relatively few of those of the thirteenth century.

Of the lyrics and melodies which remain, many have suffered varying degrees of mutilation and distortion. In some of the extant manuscripts, words and even whole lines have been omitted, passages have been so distorted as to be incomprehensible, notation has occasionally been changed, and sometimes stanzas have been added. In many cases, songs which were composed by an unknown singer, perhaps a *Spielmann,* appear in the manuscripts under the name of a famous minnesinger. One of the most common causes for the corruption of the poetic text was the fact that the minnesong was recorded in a dialect that differed greatly from the one in which it was originally composed, so that what we now have is actually a translation and often not a very accurate one. The chief causes of corruption of the musical text were again that many tunes were preserved for a long time only by oral transmission, that those written down preserved only the pitch of the melody, and that the written text could not preserve the improvisational aspects of the performance tradition through which they were handed down. However, in spite of losses, mutilations, and corruption, there are still several thousand minnesong texts extant in a good state of preservation. They represent the work of some 150 minnesingers. Although the loss of melodies was even more severe, there are still about 450 minnesong tunes extant, quite enough to present an adequate picture of the music of the time.

The extant minnesongs appear in nearly fifty manuscripts and fragments of manuscripts, some containing several hundred songs, a few containing only one or two. The oldest of the larger manuscripts, the Old Heidelberg manuscript, was compiled by four successive scribes during the period from the late thirteenth century to the end of the fourteenth century. The collection includes lyrics by thirty-four minnesingers but has no music notation. The next important collection, which also has no music, is the Weingarten manuscript. It was prepared at the beginning of the fourteenth century and includes songs by thirty-one minnesingers, twenty-five of whom

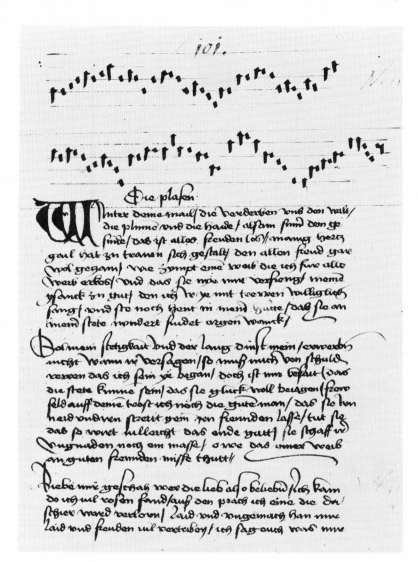

Ms. germ. fol. 779, Bl. 231ʳ, Stiftung Preussischer Kulturbesitz, Depot der Staatsbibliothek, Tübingen.

thing (in some cases all that is known) of the lives and positions of their subjects. No melodies are included. From the standpoint of the musician the most important manuscript is the Jena manuscript, which was prepared about the middle of the fourteenth century and contains primarily religious and didactic songs, for most of which there is music notation. The songs of thirty composers appear in this manuscript, and there are over seventy pages of music. Second only to the Jena manuscript in importance to the musician is the Vienna manuscript (Nationalbibliothek, Hs. 2701), prepared in the fourteenth century, which contains about the same amount of notation as the former, though from a much smaller number of composers. Two further manuscripts, the Münster fragment and the Berlin Neidhart manuscript, are of particular significance to the musicologist because of the antiquity of the music and the importance of the composers represented. The former contains three melodies of Walther von der Vogelweide, the latter fifteen melodies of Neidhart von Reuenthal. Both manuscripts are of fairly recent origin, dating from about the middle of the fifteenth century. There are quite a few poems and some melodies which appear in more than one manuscript, always in a slightly different form. Such variance is the result either of inexact oral transmission or of careless copying of older manuscripts which have since disappeared.

The manuscripts and fragments of the works of the minnesingers have preserved a great wealth of verse and music literature, which, however, because of the Middle High German language and the neume notation in which the music appears, is not available to the general public. It is the purpose of this anthology to present in English translation and modern transcription a representative selection of minnesong from its beginning in the twelfth century to its final disappearance in the fifteenth century. The songs included not only reflect a unique and most interesting culture, but also have an intrinsic value, independent of their historical importance, as significant and permanent works of art.

are pictured in beautiful illustrations. By far the most famous of the collections is the Manesse manuscript, which was prepared during the first half of the fourteenth century. It contains songs by 139 minnesingers and has 138 excellent illustrations. Since the latter show the minnesingers in characteristic situations, they reveal some-

The Early Minnesingers

Kürenberg

THE SINGER Kürenberg was probably a member of the knightly family which occupied Kürnberg Castle, near Linz, Austria, during the twelfth century. Structurally, and perhaps also chronologically, these are the oldest of the minnesongs. Of the fifteen stanzas which have been preserved, twelve consist of two sets of rhymed couplets with long lines divided by caesuras. The remaining three stanzas have an additional short line. The single manuscript in which Kürenberg's verse appears does not group the various stanzas into poems, and we may conclude that most of them were intended as independent units. The fact that the verse structure used by Kürenberg is the same as that employed by the anonymous Austrian author of the epic poem *The Song of the Nibelungs* raises the interesting possibility that Kürenberg may have been that poet. Several lines are incomplete as they appear in the manuscript. These lines have been restored in the following texts whenever it has been clear which words were omitted.

The verse of Kürenberg is distinguished by a charming simplicity of language and feeling. He does not sing of the *minne* of the classical minnesingers, but of natural, naive emotions. His women are not remote and unattainable, but warm and affectionate and eager to love and be loved.

The Loveliest of Women Is Still a Little Maid
(*Aller wibe wunne diu gêt noch magetîn*)[1]

The most popular form of love poem in medieval Latin literature was the epistle. This does not appear in the songs of the minnesingers, for it was a completely oral art, but the message and the messenger are of frequent occurrence. It is characteristic of Kürenberg, and of the earliest minnesingers in general, that assonance often appears instead of pure rhyme.

The loveliest of women is still a little maid;
I'll send to her a message in words of fondest praise,

[1]The Middle High German lyric texts for this anthology have been obtained for the most part from published collections which are not consistent with each other in their manner of reproducing the manuscripts, some using *i*, *f*, *uo*, for example, where *y*, *v*, *u* appear in the originals. Some editors have also added circumflex signs to indicate long vowels.

I'd go myself, if certain   it would not cause her woe.
I wonder if she loves me;   no maid has pleased me so.

Dear and Lovely Woman,
Journey Now with Me
(Wîp vil schône,   nu var du sam mir)

The belief that Kürenberg had never been exposed to the conventions of courtly love is supported by this simple and appealing declaration, addressed not to a "lady" but to a woman.

Dear and lovely woman,   journey now with me,
happiness and sorrow   I will share with thee.
So long as I have hold on life   so faithful will I
    prove
and grant thee all, and ever   be constant in my
    love.

The Misty Star of Evening
Glows and Quickly Dies
(Der tunkel sterne [sich]   der birget sich)

The need for secrecy, which appears in this poem, was to become an accepted convention in the later minnesong. However, with regard to the secrecy theme, Kürenberg was certainly no innovator, since it appears in much of the medieval Latin love verse.

The misty star of evening   glows and quickly dies,
as does your glance, fair lady,   when it meets my
    eyes.
And then you turn your face away   toward anyone
    you see,
so none can guess the secret   you share with only
    me.

When I Am in My Nightgown,
Alone and Lonely Here
(Swenne ich stân al eine   in mînem hemede)

In the later minnesong the lover's plaint is almost always voiced by a knight. In about half of Kürenberg's

verse, however, the speaker is a woman. She, rather than the knight, is the lonely or forsaken one.

When I am in my nightgown,   alone and lonely
    here,
and when I think of thee,   my noble cavalier,
my color turns to crimson   as the rosebud on the
    thorn,
and then within my bosom   such sad desire is born.

To Be Toward Friends a Stranger
Causes Grief and Pain
(Vil lieber vriund [vremden]   daz ist schedelîch)

The lines are the plaint of a woman who is speaking to a messenger.

To be toward friends a stranger   causes grief and
    pain:
who's ever true to loved ones   merits praise and
    fame.
I like this common saying.
Go, bid him still be faithful   now as in the past,
remind him of what we promised   when I saw him
    last.

Why Speak of Coming Sorrow,
Thou Most Dear to Me?
(Wes manstu mich leides,   mîn vil [liebe] liep)

The theme of eternal constancy is another which became a convention with the later minnesingers. However, here it is a woman who is faithful, and in the classical minnesong it is always the knight. Some scholars believe that the short line which appears here and in the previous song was due to faulty transmission and was not in the song as Kürenberg composed it.

Why speak of coming sorrow,   thou most dear to
    me?
That we should part forever,   that must never be.
If I should lose thy favor,
then I would let the people   clearly understand
how little is my pleasure   in any other man.

Care Will Change to Sorrow   Every Fond Delight
(*Leit machet sorge,   vil liep wunne*)

The theme of the jealous enemies who spy on lovers was a common one in medieval Latin writings and became popular among the later minnesingers.

> Care will change to sorrow   every fond delight:
> I became acquainted   with a handsome knight;
> that they drove him forth from me,   the spies
>   with evil art,
> has robbed me of my joy   and left a heavy heart.

I Raised Myself a Falcon   Longer Than a Year
(*Ich zôch mir einen valken   mêre danne ein jar*)

At least two of the stanzas of Kürenberg definitely belong together.[2] They form his best-known song. Although the song is about a falcon, it also tells us something of the lonely woman in whose mouth the lines are placed. She sees the contrast between the freedom of the falcon and her own position, separated from the one she loves.

> I raised myself a falcon   longer than a year.
> I tamed and made him gentle   as I would have
>   him be,
> and wove among his feathers   slender golden
>   strands,
> he mounted up toward heaven   and flew to other
>   lands.

> I later saw the falcon   flying swift and strong,
> And fastened to his talons   he wore a silken thong,
> his wings and coat of feathers   gleamed with red
>   and gold.
> May God bring those together   who gladly would
>   their lovers hold.

No music has survived for Kürenberg's verse. However, the fact that he used a typically epic rather than a lyric form may throw some light on the manner of the performance. The singer may have used a flexible, repetitive formula which he could vary in an improvisatory manner. Unfortunately no music for any German epic poetry employing epic form has survived, which suggests that the formulas used by the singer were so simple and stereotyped that there was no need to write them down, and their manner of performance could be taken completely for granted, even after the lyric began to be written down.

It is possible that the same basic tune was used for all of Kürenberg's poems, since the manuscript in which they appear—the Manesse manuscript—introduces each poem of his with the same color of capital letter. Different *Töne* in the works of other poets are consistently indicated in the manuscript by differently colored initial capital letters.

---

[2]When they form a narrative unit, all of the stanzas which the minnesingers set to a single melody appear in this anthology as one song. When they do not, as is usually the case with the *Sprüche*, they are treated as separate songs.

Spervogel

ACCORDING to tradition, the songs which appear under the pseudonym Spervogel (Sparrow) were composed by two separate singers, the "Older" and the "Younger" Spervogel; and tradition has some support from the fact that two slightly different *Töne* were employed. With regard to language and content, however, the two groups of poems are quite similar. We know nothing of the lives of either of the Spervogels. It is quite likely that they were wandering singers, probably Bavarians, of humble station. They were approximately contemporary with Kürenberg.

The Spervogel songs all consist of a single stanza, and are of a didactic nature; that is, they are *Sprüche* rather than true minnesongs. The texts are characterized by simplicity of form, concise and often forceful language, and an imaginative use of homely metaphors and symbols. They contain a wealth of genuinely religious and moral wisdom, sometimes expressed in short parables and animal fables.

A Wolf Was Fearful for His Soul
(*Ein wolf sîne sünde vlôch*)

In addition to illustrating the saying "Once a wolf, always a wolf," the singer shows a keen awareness of the excesses of some of the clergy of the time. The song is ascribed to the "Older" Spervogel.

> A wolf was fearful for his soul,
> he joined a cloister, donned a stole:
> this life he much preferred.
> They sent him out to guard the herd
> and he forgot his creed.
> He tore the sheep and swine
>   and swore the bishop's dog had done the deed.

Listen to What the Hedgehog Said
(*Weistu wie der igel sprach*)

The life of wandering singers was often difficult, and many songs were composed which expressed their longing for a place of their own and their resentment at the lack of generosity of their patrons.

Swa eyn vriunt dem andern vriunde bigestat

Listen to what the hedgehog said:
"It's nice to have a home and bed."
Build you a house, my boy,
seek there for peace and joy.
The lords are miserly.
Who doesn't have a house and home
   much happiness will never see.

When a Friend Will Always
Stand Beside His Friend

(Swa eyn vriunt dem andern vriunde bigestat)

The final couplet of long lines divided by caesuras distinguishes the stanza below from the two preceding songs and marks it as the work of the "Younger" Spervogel. Several other Spervogel songs have been composed on the theme of friendship.

When a friend will always stand beside his friend
with loyal hand and heart whenever woes descend,
then is his willing hand an aid
to him whose friendship is repaid,
and when they each support the other,   then
   their strength increases.
When friends will help each other   they have
   joy which never ceases.

Like so many of the songs of the Jena manuscript, Spervogel's *Spruch* shows evidence in its musical form of the oral tradition by which it was handed down. In the music, the long lines of the couplet at the end of the stanza are treated as two lines each, so that the musical pattern has eight rather than six lines. The last three lines are a varied repetition of lines 3–5, which does not correspond to the poetic form, but causes the repetition to begin at the caesura of the first line of the couplet, producing the musical form AB CDE C'D'E'. This might be a corruption of an earlier version of the song which might originally have repeated the melody for the second long line of the closing couplet.

The manner in which the phrases are varied in the repetition suggests that the scribe notated it as the singer happened to sing it, and that the singer felt free to ornament the lines. The up-beats of lines 3 and 6 show the addition of an ornament for the second statement of the melody, while the two different cadences of lines 5 and 8 give the effect of open and closed endings.

This is the only one of the many Spervogel songs for which the music has survived. It is possible that the other songs of the "Younger" Spervogel may have had a melodic repetition of some kind associated with the long closing couplet of the verse form he favored.

Dietmar von Aist

Dietmar belonged to a noble Austrian family whose castle stood on the Alt-Aist Mountain near the Enns River. He is mentioned in various records from 1143 to 1171.

The history of the German lyric, insofar as it has been preserved, begins with Dietmar, for Kürenberg composed and probably performed his works in an epic rather than a lyric style, and Spervogel's verse is composed of *Sprüche* rather than *Lieder*. Dietmar's songs are particularly interesting because of the definite development which they reveal. The earlier ones have parallel, often impure, rhyme and show the naiveté of Kürenberg and Spervogel. The later songs have pure rhyme, a slightly more intricate rhyme pattern, the beginnings of a stanzaic structure, and reveal something of the formalized and sophisticated tone of the classical minnesong. However, even in his later period, Dietmar does not sing of *minne* but of physical love, and it is still the lady rather than the knight who seeks to win favor with the loved one, who weeps for loneliness, and who shows devotion and constancy. Dietmar probably never came into direct contact with Provençal verse, and the development in his art is perhaps due rather to the influence of the songs of wandering clerics. Two types of minnesongs appear for the first time with Dietmar: the alternating song and the dawn song.

Gay Summer's Bliss, Goodbye
(*So wôl dir sumerwunne*)

The lady says farewell to summer and to her sweetheart, who is departing on a long journey. The identification of emotions with the seasons, spring or summer with joy and winter with loneliness or sorrow, was to become a commonplace with the later minnesingers. As is illustrated in the translation, the rhymes of the poem are pure as far as vowels are concerned, but the consonant rhyme is imperfect.

Gay summer's bliss, goodbye!
The bird's sweet song has died,
the linden's leaves are gone,
the fading year beyond

will make these fair eyes weary.
My love, hear this entreaty:
all other charms
avoid, and other arms.
The moment that you met me
Your manly form impressed me,
I thought you wondrous fair—
so, lover dear, beware!

A Lady Stood Alone
(*Es stuont ein frouwe aleine*)

The objects of nature, especially birds and flowers,
appear frequently in Dietmar's verse, often with symbolic
significance. The falcon in the poem, as in the falcon song
of Kürenberg, is a symbol of freedom. In these references
to nature is seen the embryo of the nature preface of the
later minnesong.

A lady stood alone
and looked out on the plain
and waited for her love;
she saw a falcon high above.
"Lucky falcon there on high!
Whither you wish you fly;
you choose from the forest trees
whichever one you please.
So I too have done:
I chose myself a man,
my two eyes did agree.
But charming women envy me.
Oh, why do they set their snares?
I never wanted a lover of theirs."

Page of My Languishing Sweetheart,
Now Say to the Lady Fair
(*Seneder friundinne bote,   nu sage dem schône wîbe*)

This song and those which follow belong to Dietmar's
later period. It is an "alternating song," in which a knight
and his faraway sweetheart in turn address a messenger.

The influence of medieval Latin verse is seen particularly
in the salutation which introduces each of the messages.

"Page of my languishing sweetheart,   now say to
    the lady fair,
my absence from her has caused me grief   and
    sorrow beyond compare.
I would rather have her love
than songs of all the birds above.
Now that we must stay so long apart
deepest sadness seizes all my heart."
"Just say to the knight so noble,   that I do wish
    him well,
and bid him ever be full of joy,   and all his fears
    dispel.
I so often for him must pine,
which sorely troubles this heart of mine.
All I see about me gives me pain,
of this I'll speak when once we meet again."

Still Sleeping, Handsome Knight?
(*Slafestu, vriedel ziere*)

This, the first dawn song of German music, well illustrates the painstaking symmetry which the minnesingers
gave their verse. The first eight lines make up the rising
song with its two *Stollen* of equal length; the last four lines
form the falling song. In the first *Stollen*, in which a lady
speaks, the word "sleeping" in the first line parallels
"Awake! Awake!" in the second line, while objects of
nature, the birds and the linden tree, appear in parallel
in the third and fourth lines. These two symbols of happiness contrast with the sorrow implied in the first half of
the first *Stollen*.

In the second *Stollen* (lines 5 to 8), in which a knight is
speaking, it will be noted that the first two lines parallel
the first two lines of the first *Stollen*. "I slept gently"
answers "Still sleeping?" and "you give the alarm" corresponds to "Take flight!" The first two lines of the second
Stollen also contrast with each other as "love" contrasts
with "sorrow" in the following line. Both emotions are

resolved in the concept of service and duty which is presented in the last line of the second *Stollen* (line 8).

The concluding four lines, the falling song, present the real theme of the poem, which is the lament of the lady at the departure of her lover. The rising song merely sets the scene for this outpouring of sorrow. Similar symmetrical patterns will be observed in other minnesongs.

"Still sleeping, handsome knight?
Awake! Awake! Take flight!
A bird in all its finery
warns us from the linden tree."
"I slept gently on your arm,
and now, sweetheart, you give the alarm;
but love must have its sorrow too,
what you command I'll quickly do."
The lady then began to moan,
"You ride and leave me all alone.
When will you ever return to me?
With you my joys and pleasures flee."

Yonder on the Linden Tree
There Sang a Merry Little Bird
(Ûf der linden obene   dâ sanc ein kleinez vogellîn)

This is an alternating song which voices first the thoughts of the knight and then those of his faraway sweetheart. In the song one can see how objects of nature have become definite artistic conventions. The linden is summer, the bird is life and happiness, the rose is love. The knight is reminded of the lady, who combines these characteristics. In the second *Stollen* the lady presents the same symbols in connection with the knight, whom she has not seen for so long. The over-all symbolism is, of course, the summer-winter, joy-sorrow pattern which can be seen in a great number of minnesongs.

"Yonder on the linden tree   there sang a merry
   little bird.
Its voice rang out at the forest's edge   and then my
   heart, by memory stirred,
returned to a place that it once knew.   I saw the
   roses gently blow;

they bring a host of thoughts about   a certain
   lady that I know."
"It seems at least a thousand years   since in my
   lover's arms I lay;
and I am not to blame that he   has left me now
   for many a day.
Since then I've seen no flowers bloom   and heard
   no bird's enchanting song,
since then my joy has been short-lived,   my pain
   and sorrow all too long."

The Winter Such a Time Would Be
(Der winter waere mir ein zît)

Although this song appears in one manuscript under the name of Heinrich von Veldeke, it is generally attributed to Dietmar. The song has two characteristics which connect it with the later minnesong: alternating rhyme in place of rhymed couplets and a love plaint by a man instead of a woman. Dietmar uses this *Ton* for several other poems, but there is little reason to assume that he intended them as separate stanzas in a single work.

The winter such a time would be
of wondrous happiness and bliss
were but a lady here with me
to still my yearning with a kiss.
I'd bless the longest winter night,
if I could spend it by her side,
but now so wretched is my plight
with sorrow that I cannot hide.

Gennrich believes this to be a contrafact of a melody by Ventadorn and has made three quite different transcriptions of it. It is, of course, possible that Dietmar borrowed the music, but it must be remembered that there was little direct contact between Austria and Provence at the time that Dietmar was composing. As far as inner evidence is concerned, the metrical system and the content are commonplace enough, and there are other melodies which fit the metrical system and other songs which have a similar theme. While the songs of Ventadorn were widely known and could have been transmitted to Dietmar by a

Der winter waere mir ein zît

Der win - ter wae - re mir ein zît so reh - te wun - nec-
"Wie tuot der bes - ten ei – nen so daz er mîn se - nen

lî - che guot, wurd ich sô sae - lic daz ein wîp ge-
mac ver-tra-gen? Ez wae - re wol, und wurde ich frô: sich

trôs - te mî - nen sen – den muot. Sô
kun - de nie - man baz ge - ha - ben. Wê

wol mich dan - ne lan - ger naht, ge - laege ich alse ich
daz mir leit von dem ge - schiht der an mîn herze ist

wil - len hân! Si hât mich in ein trû - ren brâht des
nâ - he ko-men! Waz hil - fet zorn? Swenn er mich siht, den

ich mich niht ge – mâ – zen kan.
hât er schie - re mir be - no - men."

Contrafact of "Can vei la lauzeta mover," Bernart de Ventadorn. Source of melody, Paris, B.N., Fonds fr. 844, *Manuscrit du Roi,* f. 190.

wandering cleric, it seems doubtful that the rhythm of the original would have been transmitted unchanged. Even though Ventadorn's song might have had a modal rhythm, the rhythm of Gennrich's latest transcription,[3] which begins each line with one dactylic foot instead of using an up-beat, is very dubious. The transcription given here abandons Gennrich's emphasis on triple rhythm and uses a free rhythm instead.

[3]Friedrich Gennrich, *Anthology of Music,* Vol. II: *Troubadours, Trouvères, Minnesang and Meistergesang* (Köln, Arno Volk, 1960), p. 45.

Friedrich von Hausen

FRIEDRICH VON HAUSEN was a prominent man of his day. He was known in the imperial court and mentioned rather frequently in twelfth-century records. He was born in the Rhineland, possibly in the neighborhood of Mainz, about the year 1155. He is first mentioned in 1175, when he accompanied the Archbishop of Mainz to Italy, which country he visited a second time in 1186 as a part of the retinue of the emperor Friedrich I (Barbarossa). The following year he was in France and present at a historically important meeting between the emperor and King Philippe-Auguste. Two years later, in 1189, he departed with the emperor on the Third Crusade and died in Syria in 1190.

Because of its position at the junction of the Rhine and Main rivers, Mainz in the twelfth century was the chief center of trade and cultural interchange between the German-speaking and French-speaking peoples. Here, as well as on his travels to Italy and France, Hausen became acquainted with Provençal songs and with the chivalric concepts and themes which they expressed. Although he was the first of the minnesingers to be clearly influenced by the troubadours, he was not merely an imitator, but the creator of an art distinctly his own. The distinctive element in Hausen's verse results primarily from his strong religious feeling and his effort to form an inner relationship between religion and *minne*. He rejects the frank desire for sexual satisfaction which appears in Dietmar and veils erotic elements with abstract expressions. For Hausen, beauty appears as the creation of God, and it cannot therefore be sinful for man to love it, but physical attractiveness must be accompanied by virtuousness if it is to be beautiful. In his songs the concept of *minne* becomes less sensuous and more spiritualized; *minne* and religion are combined in a Christian ethic.

Fifty-five stanzas of Hausen are extant. They show the influence of Bernart de Ventadorn, Folquet de Marseille, and Conon de Bethune. Although none of his music is extant, there is strong internal evidence in some of his songs that he used certain Romance melodies.

Deich von der guoten schiet

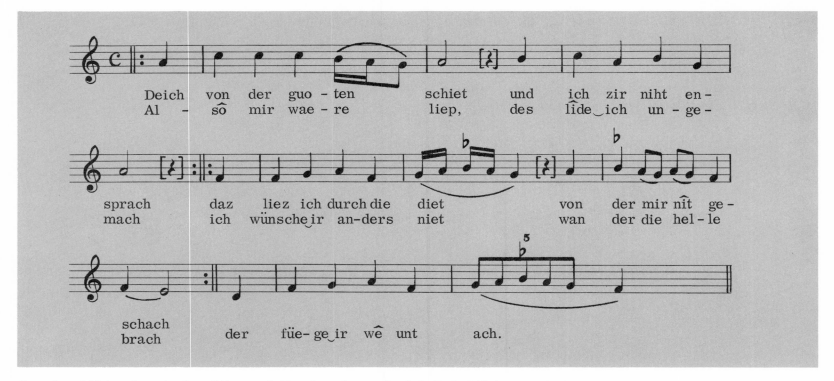

Contrafact of "Pois prejatz mi, seignor," Bernart de Ventadorn. Source of melody, Paris, B.N. fr. 22543, f. 57.

That I Should Go Away
(Deich von der guoten schiet)

The following alternating song sings not of passion but of true love, temporarily frustrated by the "jealous ones" and the "guardians." With the latter group Hausen introduces a new element into the minnesong, but the identity of these guardians here, as also in later minnesong, remains vague. It is interesting that none of the minnesingers refers to a jealous husband.

"That I should go away
and give her no farewell,
although I wished to stay,
is grief I cannot tell.
They led me thus astray
who would my love dispel;
I hope they get their pay
from him who rules in hell;

there may they ever dwell."
"These guardians of mine
would rescue me from woe.
I see their foul design,
they'll not succeed, I know.
They'd sooner turn the Rhine
to empty in the Po
and make the streams combine
before I'd let him go
who always loved me so."

The melodies which are used for Hausen's songs are all contrafacts, and examples from various sources are given here. Each one has been transcribed according to a different rhythmic theory to illustrate the effects of various approaches to rhythmic transcription. The wide variety of effects which this produces is indicative of the disagree-

ment of scholars, but it may even have a historical validity
of its own, since during the period when these songs were
preserved largely by oral tradition, it is likely that several
rhythmic styles were used by the singers, varying with
geographical location and local taste, and perhaps
influenced by the style of other music of the time. Although
the singers might have kept the rhythms of the French
models or contrafacts at first (and, of course, the nature of
these rhythms is also highly controversial), these may have
been adapted in various ways to German tastes as time
passed.

"Deich von der guoten schiet" has been transcribed in
duple meter with each ligature within a phrase given one
beat and the final note of ligatures in cadences lengthened.
The ligatures show characteristic ornamental patterns.
Two versions of this tune exist, both with the same text,
that of Bernart de Ventadorn's "Pois prejatz mi, seignor."[4]
Though they follow the same general melodic contours,
the version given here is in Lydian mode, while the other
version is in Aeolian, and the ornaments also vary
considerably. This suggests that the transmission of the
mode in the secular songs was quite casual. The musical
form of the song is AA BB C in both versions.

The Sweetest Words Which Ever I
(*Diu süezen wort hânt mir getân*)

The unrequited love of a knight for a lady, one of the
most popular themes of the minnesingers, first appears in
German verse with Hausen. It was a part of the Provençal
tradition from which he drew. Another influence of the
troubadours on Hausen can be seen in the virtuosity of
his recurring rhyme and his conscious use of a polystrophic
structure.

The sweetest words which ever I
have heard from people I have known
are all of her, and that is why
my love for her has always grown.
My other cares are small, I own,
compared to that for which I sigh.
In all the world beneath the sky,

God knows, I love but her alone.
My suit deserves a fair reply.

Of all the women God has dressed
with shapely form and pleasing air
he's granted her his very best;
there's none so charming, none so fair.
What though my love is sometimes care,
with joy it often fills my breast.
My life would then be fully blessed,
if she would rue her sins, forbear
to pain me till I'm sore distressed.

Whatever pleasures God has made
are not increased through her for me,
my sorrow she has not allayed,
nor given answer to my plea.
A hardened heart has let her be
so cruel that she's never swayed
by all the grief which I've displayed
and cannot longer bear. Thus she
my love and loyalty repaid.

The music to "Diu süezen wort hânt mir getân" is
transcribed in first mode. The freedom with which up-
beats are added or omitted at the beginning and in line 6 is
quite characteristic of this whole body of song. Similar
free treatment of the up-beat occurs in the other stanzas.

She Can Never Say of Me
(*Si darf mich des zîhen niet*)

Although Friedrich von Hausen's rhyme patterns are
quite sophisticated in comparison with those of Kürenberg
and Dietmar, he resembles the older singers in that he
frequently uses assonance instead of pure rhyme, as is
indicated in the translation by the rhyming of "sleep" and
"greet." Two stanzas of the song have been omitted.

She can never say of me,
I did not love her tenderly.
The truth of this she ought to recognize,

[4]Paris, B.N. fr. 22543, f. 57, and Milan, Bibl. Ambrosiana, R. 71, Sup.

Diu süezen wort hânt mir getân

Contrafact of "D'amors ke m'ait tolut a moy," Chrétien de Troyes. Source of melody, Paris, Arsenal 5198, f. 58.

Si darf mich des zîhen niet

Contrafact of "En chantan m'aven a membrar," Folquet de Marseille. Source of melody, Milan, Ambrosiana, R. 71, Sup., f. 5.

not close her eyes.
I often suffered such distress
that I would say "Good morning," I confess,
when eve was nigh.
So lost in thoughts of her was I
that I would often walk as if in sleep
and never hear a word when friends would greet.

I served a lady with heart and sword,
but all my love brought no reward.
And still I speak of her with only praise,
although her gaze
has never yet been turned to me in kindness.
I fancied I was free of passion's blindness,
but, still in bands,
my heart sought favor from her hands,
which it has never gotten, I must say.
I'll serve Him now who will my love repay.

From love I've only known despair
and happiness was something rare.
But, though my heart with bitter pain was stirred,
no one has heard
my lips a single censure tell,
for I have always spoken women well.
Still I regret
that I could God so long forget.
I'll serve Him first of all and only then
shall I to ladies yield my heart again.

Curt Sachs[5] believes that since the French verse of the medieval lyric is numerical rather than metrical, there is doubt about the validity of the modal theories espoused by Gennrich for the rhythmic transcription of the music. He suggests instead some sort of free rhythm. "Si darf mich des zîhen niet" illustrates the effect of this approach, with each separate note transcribed as a quarter note and each ligature as a group of two, three, or four eighth notes. The flexibility of this approach leaves the singer free to give a rhythmically expressive treatment to such highly ornamented lines as line 9, which has a particularly lovely series of "sighing" two- and three-note patterns. The end of each phrase is lengthened slightly, at the discretion of the singer. Since this solution is essentially a framework for a performance, it cannot be notated exactly; thus, the execution will be expressive of the singer's taste and may freely depart from the rhythm of the approximation given here. If this was the approach used by the minnesingers themselves, it would explain why the songs were notated in an archaic, rhythmically noncommittal script at a time when other forms of notation were available.

Now and Then I Ponder
(Ich denke under wilen)

The tripartite structure of the minnesong did not disappear with the development of stanzaic structure and frequently both forms exist in the same song, as in the verses below. Here each stanza can be divided into two *Stollen* and a falling song. One stanza has been omitted.

Now and then I ponder
o'er that which I'd be saying
if she were here with me.
It shortens roads I wander
to let my thoughts go straying
to her with plaint and plea.
But when the people see
my face, they think I'm playing,
so gay I seem to be
to hide my misery.

Had I not undertaken
a love so high as ours,
I might perhaps find aid.
I did it when forsaken
by sense, now care devours
each happy plan I've made.
For loyalty has swayed
my will and overpowers
a heart that would have strayed
when hopes had been betrayed.

Whatever may betide me
one joy I'll always treasure
and never let it go:
to dream of her beside me,

[5]Sachs, *Rhythm and Tempo*, p. 178.

Ich denke under wîlen

Contrafact of "Ma joie premerainne," Guiot de Provins. Source of melody, Paris, B.N. fr. 20050, f. 17.

*In these two cadences the ligatures of the original must be broken to accommodate the feminine endings of the German text.

though distant lands I measure.
This comfort she'll bestow.
If she would have it so,
the greater is my pleasure;
no other man I know
such constancy would show.

This song displays a complicated musical form in which sections of the second *Stollen* of the stanza are repeated freely in the *Abgesang:* AA'B CDE E'C'D'E". On the rhyme words *waere, swaere,* and *gebaere* (lines 2, 5, and 8) the same ornament pattern is used for the musical cadence, although each word is in a different part of the formal scheme given above. Such close correspondence between details of the text and the music is a strong indication of the likelihood that this is indeed the tune to which Friedrich von Hausen wrote his text. This is one of the few texts using the traditional tripartite structure which does not repeat the music of the first *Stollen* for the second *Stollen*.

Alas, My Heart Is Sore
(*Mir ist daz herze wunt*)

In addition to a sincere religious feeling, there are two other characteristics which appear in most of Hausen's songs: kindliness and sensibleness. His kindliness causes him to wish the lady in the song happiness, although she has not returned his affection. His good sense makes him feel that his heart has been most foolish to choose one who will not love him. In effect, he questions the basic principle of courtly love.

> Alas, my heart is sore
> and has been sick for many a year,
> 'twas not a fool before
> it learned to know a lady here,
> but should the king himself appear
> and place a kiss or more
> on lips which I adore,
> he'd swear, he'd never known their peer.
>
> My heart I gave away
> to one who ranks among the best,
> and would receive my pay,

if she would grant me one request.
But though my suit has not been blessed,
though she no love display,
my hope is that she may
have more of joy than all the rest.

Who better could relieve
my pain than could the lady fair
who taught me how to grieve
with sorrow none can see nor share.
Still I deserve the pain I bear:
such hopes I should not weave.
If Love can thus deceive,
then every lover must beware.

The normal repeats of the first section of the musical form are distorted here by changes which may have originated in a scribal error. The beginning of the fourth line, which originally may have corresponded with the second line, seems to have been written on the wrong staff line, giving a variant version beginning a third lower than the line is supposed to repeat. The variation in the cadence of the first and third lines may have arisen from the same error. The rhythmic transcription uses the principle of free rhythm.

I See What Wonders God Can Do
(*Ich sihe wol, daz got wunder kan*)

In this poem Hausen introduces a device, the refrain, which was adopted by many of the later minnesingers. He may have obtained the refrain either from troubadour songs or from Latin hymns. Since both liturgical music and dance forms use refrains as choral responses, one could surmise that Hausen's listeners readily understood that they were supposed to sing with him the final couplet of each stanza.

> I see the wonders God can do
> of lovely works in human form.
> My lady's showed, when He was through,
> that He forgot no single charm.
> The grief she causes me, the harm,
> that will I bear, and gladly too,

Mir ist daz herze wunt

Mir ist daz her - ze wunt und siech ge - we - sen

nu vil lan - ge (deis reht: wan ez ist tump), sitz

ei - ne fro - wen êrst be - kan - de, der kei - ser ist in

al - len lan - den, kust er si zei - ner stunt an

ir vil rô - ten munt, er jae - he ez wae - re im wol er - gan - gen.

Contrafact of "Mult m'a demoré," anonymous trouvère. Source of melody, Paris, B.N., n.a. fr. 1050, f. 253.

*Manuscript has *a g* here.

**Manuscript has one more *c* here.

***The missing notes are supplied from the other two manuscript versions: Paris, Arsenal 5198, f. 394, and Paris, B.N. fr. 846, f. 83.

Note that up-beats must be supplied for almost every phrase to fit the additional light syllables in the German poem.

so I may stay and in her arms
have all my fondest dreams come true.
Whate'er she does, my love shall see
that she'll not soon be rid of me.

Let her not think that I bestow
my love in passing or in play.
While still a child and long ago,
to her I gave my heart away
and have been faithful since the day
I first began to love her so.
My heart, still subject to her sway,
eternal loyalty will show.
Whate'er she does, my love shall see
that she'll not soon be rid of me.

It is indeed unfortunate that the music for the minnesongs with refrains has all been lost, so that it is not possible to describe the musical treatment of this device. This
is particularly distressing since refrain forms were of such
great importance in the Romance sources which influenced this group of minnesingers.

They Seek to Escape from Death and Pain

(Sie wânent dem tôde entrunnen sin)

For one of Hausen's religious nature the obligation
to support the Third Crusade was unequivocal, and it is
not surprising that he was the composer of the first German
crusade songs. It is characteristic of Hausen that he ap-
peals neither to love of adventure nor to hate of the enemy,
but to duty to God. No melody for the song is known, but
it is not unlikely that it was sung to the tune of a hymn.

They seek to escape from death and pain
who take no part in God's crusade,
but this I know: their hope is vain
and they have but themselves betrayed.
Who took the cross and gave no aid
will find in death his error plain
and stand before the gate, dismayed,
which opens wide for God's true thane.

Heinrich von Veldeke

HEINRICH VON VELDEKE was born of a knightly family in the lower Rhineland area in the vicinity of Maastricht. About the year 1170 he was living at the court of the Duke of Cleve, where he composed *The Legend of Saint Servatius,* an adaptation from a Latin source. Sometime in the following ten years he moved to the court of Count Hermann of Thuringia, the famous patron of the minnesong. It was at the latter's castle at Neuenberg that Veldeke composed his best-known work, his *Eneit,* the first of the German courtly epics. Although the poem is based on the *Aeneid,* the immediate source was not Vergil's work, but that of a Frenchman, Benoit de Sainte-Maure. In 1184 Veldeke was the chief musical performer at the imperial festival at Mainz, arranged by Friedrich I on the occasion of the knighting of his two sons. It is estimated that as many as fifty thousand people—nobles, knights, and minstrels—from all points of the Empire may have attended the festival, the most grandiose and colorful spectacle of medieval times. Veldeke became at once the most famous and influential minnesinger in Germany. His influence was exerted in the direction of pure rhyme, regular rhythm, and a stricter and more artistic form. His contemporary, Gottfried von Strassburg, praises him in the courtly epic *Tristan and Isolde* as the one who grafted the first twig in the German language from which the branches sprang and the blossoms came. Certainly at the court of Hermann (who was reared in France) and probably before then, Veldeke had heard Provençal and French singers and had fully assimilated their art and concepts. It is with him that the tradition of *Frauendienst* and the cult of *minne* really begins. *Minne* becomes the greatest of aesthetic and cultural values and the source of all virtues. Indeed, in the verse of Veldeke, in contrast to that of Hausen, one might say that the ethic of *minne* replaces the Christian ethic.

Veldeke's songs have neither the naive charm and frank sensuousness of Dietmar nor the depth of feeling of Hausen. His characters are involved in a pleasant social game which he describes in light-hearted, sometimes even humorous, language. Veldeke depicts nature to a greater extent than did his predecessors; indeed, he developed such descriptions to a formal convention, the "nature introduction," but one does not feel that he was actually closely drawn to nature.

Veldeke died before 1210. Fifty-five stanzas of his lyric verse survive, but none of his melodies. However, some of the songs will fit trouvère melodies, and it may be assumed that these were the tunes he used. Although Veldeke composed his songs in Low German, they appear in the manuscripts only in High German. However, scholars have translated them back into their original form, which is that quoted in the following section.

I Beg Thee, Love, Whose Yoke I Don
(*Die minne bite ich ende man*)

Veldeke sings in a light and somewhat facetious tone, not to a sweetheart, but to the spirit of courtly love.

> I beg thee, Love, whose yoke I don,
> who has captured me as a prize,
> that thou mayest hurry my sweetheart on
> to better reward my sighs.
> For should I fare as doth the swan,
> who sings his melody and dies,
> I would pay too much for the joy I've won.

Tristan, Not from His Desire
(*Tristrant moeste sonder danc*)

The story of Tristan and Isolde was one of the most popular subjects of medieval romance. It originated with an unknown French poet of the twelfth century and was widely disseminated by the end of the century.

> Tristan, not from his desire,
> served the queen with true devotion,
> subject to a lover's fire
> less than to a magic potion.
> Therefore should my lady thank
> me, for though I never drank
> such a brew, my heart's emotion
> equals that from witch's wine.
> Thing of beauty, truth and duty,
> grant that I be thine
> and that thou be mine!

When the Seasons Thus Decree
(*Swen die tîd also gestât*)

In the twelfth century, before the days of stoves, lamps, and glass windows, the winter was a dreary time, even for the knights. It is little wonder that much of the verse of the minnesingers celebrates the joys of spring.

> When the seasons thus decree
> that grass may green and flowers bloom,
> my heart will then at last be free
> from all that burdened it with gloom.
> The birds would rejoice, and not alone,
> if summer always would remain.
> Though the world were all my own,
> the winter still would cause me pain.

When the Summer Sun Is Chill
(*Sît die sonne her liechten skîn*)

Besides the many spring and summer songs, there were winter songs, usually expressions of sadness and loneliness, such as this one. In the poem Veldeke introduces rhymed half-lines, "brilliant shade pale and fade," a metrical device which was employed by most of his successors.

> When the summer sun is chill
> and before the winter cowers,
> when the songs of birds are still
> in the field and woodland bowers,
> sadness then my heart will fill
> for it won't be long until
> winter shows to us its powers.
> In the blossoms we shall see
> brilliant shade pale and fade;
> this will bring to me
> no joy, but misery.

So Kind Is She and Oh So Fair
(*Sî is so gût ende ouch so scône*)

Although Veldeke accepts and upholds the code of chivalry and courtly love, he sometimes cannot restrain his impulse to poke fun at it. He does this in the third stanza, where he intimates that although *minne* is fine, money is even better.

So kind is she and oh, so fair
whom I have often praised ere now,
had I the crown of Rome to wear
I'd gladly place it on her brow.
"Behold, he's mad!" some folks would vow.
That she regard me is my prayer;
I know, if she is still as dear,
what I would do, if I were near,
but she is there, and I am here.

When she desired, she brought to me
so much of pleasure and delight
that I rejoice in memory
and all the joys of love recite.
For since I saw how she at night
could fool the watch as cleverly,
as hounds by hares are oft deceived,
of all my fears I've been relieved,
nor for my father's son have grieved.

I'd rather have her for my own
and have a thousand marks to hold
and a chest with many a precious stone,
finely wrought from burnished gold,
than see myself grow sick and old
afar from her and all alone.
Of that can she be really sure
and in this trust may rest secure,
that it's a truth which will endure.

I'm Glad That Each Succeeding Day
(*Ich bin vrô, sint ons die dage*)

In literally hundreds of songs the minnesingers told of lovers who complained that the object of their affections granted them no favors. This is perhaps the only song in which the other side of the picture appears. Here the lady complains of a lover who was not satisfied with a purely Platonic relationship and expresses her annoyance in a somewhat humorous vein. Two stanzas have been omitted.

"I'm glad that each succeeding day
which comes is longer and more bright."
Thus spoke a woman without dismay,
but with an unrestrained delight.
"I thank my lucky stars at night
that I've a heart which none can sway
and that no feebleness can blight
nor steal my happiness away.

"There was a time, not long ago,
when I was courted by a man
to whom much kindness I did show,
which I shall grant no more, nor can,
since he so brazenly began
to ask for favors which, I know,
I sooner shall refuse him than
he'll ever get me to bestow.

"I thought him versed in courtly art
and that is why, I must confess,
I loved him once with all my heart,
but he's quite free of such finesse.
Still, I can bear his pain, I guess,
and little care how he may smart.
He thought he'd have a great success,
but he'll have little when we part."

The principle used in the rhythmic transcription of this song is that of syllables of alternating accent all equal in time value, with extra time allowed between the many phrases with feminine endings. The mode of the song seems to fluctuate between Dorian and Mixolydian, due to the use of the *b*-natural at the end of the song.

Ich bin vrô, sint ons die dage

Contrafact of "Fine amour et bone esperance," Gace Brulé (also attributed to Pierre de Molins in Paris, B.N., Fonds fr. 844, *Manuscrit du Roi*, f. 43, and believed to be by Chatelain de Coucy by some scholars).

Source of the melody used for this transcription, Paris, B.N., Ms. fr. 846, *Manuscrit Cangé*, f. 54.

*The omission of a clef sign places the first eight notes of the phrase a third lower in the manuscript.

Rudolf von Fenis

RUDOLF II, Count of Fenis-Neuenberg, was born about the middle of the twelfth century and died in 1196. His ancestral castle was at Fenis, near Cerlier, Switzerland. His surviving eight minnesongs show that the singer was strongly influenced with regard to both metrics and themes by the songs of the Provençal bishop, Folquet de Marseille. Indeed, one might call Fenis' songs imitations of those of Folquet.

Structurally, Fenis' songs are of interest in that in them one can plainly see how the use of a Romance ten-syllable line frequently results in German dactyls. But his verse, though melodious, is too impersonal and affected to be interesting. Although his songs all deal with a languishing lover, they give us no picture of the beloved, for his plaints are directed to *minne* rather than to a woman. Some of Fenis' comparisons are concrete and effective, but these were largely borrowed from Folquet. In general, Rudolf von Fenis is important only as an intermediary between Provençal and German song.

In the translations below, one stanza has been omitted from the first song and two stanzas from the second.

Though I May Have Fancied
That Love Would Show

(*Gewan ich ze minnen ie guoten wân*)

Though I may have fancied that love would show
me favor, I've gained from it nothing but sorrow,
nor do I see how I shall profit tomorrow,
since I cannot have her nor let her go;
like one who has climbed up a tree that is shaking,
who cannot go higher for fear of its breaking
and can't make his way again down to the ground
and sits there for hours with fear and with quaking.

And I am like one who has fastened his heart
and his mind on a game that he plays till he loses
and then gives it up, but too late he so chooses.
So I, too, discovered, too late to depart
from the guile Love employed in the game she was
  playing.

Gewan ich ze minnen ie guoten wân

Contrafact of "Sitot me soi a tart aperceubutz," Folquet de Marseille. Source of melody, Milan, Bibl. Ambrosiana, R. 71, Sup. (Provençal), f. 2.

She brought me to her, my disquiet allaying
with friendliest smiles, as a debtor does
who promises much, but has no thought of paying.

The frequency of dactyls in the poem has suggested the use of the third rhythmic mode in the transcription. There are two possible ways of transcribing a dactylic foot in monophonic music: either ♩ ♪ ♪ or, using the triple divisions by which this mode was adapted for polyphonic music, ♩. ♪ ♩. The duple meter has been used for this transcription, but Gennrich has also made a satisfying transcription of the same tune using a triple division of each half of the foot.[6]

Love Has Commanded That I Should Sing
(*Minne gebiutet mir daz ich singe*)

For this song Fenis borrowed the melody of Gace Brulé's "De bone amor et de loiaul amie." His verses, too, owe something to those of the trouvère, as can be seen by a translation of two stanzas of Brulé's song: "True love and a faithful lady—the thought of these often arouses my emotions and awakens my memories to the extent that never in my life shall I forget those eyes and that form. If Cupid does not cease bending all lovers and ladies to his pleasure, I shall never be able to hope for the affection of my lady. How can I hope to find true love and a faithful lady in such soft eyes and gentle appearance as I shall never see again in my life? I must love—I cannot escape it—her whom my love shall never please. I cannot even imagine how I could win help and support from her."

Love has commanded that I should sing,
and forbids me ever to complain,
though she no comfort nor hope may bring
that my song its fitting reward should gain.
She wishes that I should give my love away
where my devotion no heart can sway
and where faithfulness offers little as pay.
I strive to leave her service, but in vain.

This is my lot, that I cannot permit
my heart forever to renounce its claim.

It is my sorrow, that I've not the wit
to give up serving one who hates my name.
I'll cherish her still, whatever may befall,
loyalty keeps me always in thrall,
and in spite of the fact that its wages are small.
Though she is vexed, I'll love her just the same.

In this transcription, two of the thirteen surviving versions of Gace Brulé's melody, "De bone amor et de loiaul amie," have been included to show the divergence of the musical text caused by copyist's changes, oral transmission, and so forth. It is interesting to speculate on what caused the scribe to choose the details he used in each instance. Variant versions of a tune, even when there exists a prior written source from which variants are drawn, may result from a great number of factors: scribal errors or inaccuracies in copying, deliberate changes by the scribe or collector of the tune, or the rendering of an oral tradition which had begun to change the tune since it previously had been written down. Few such comparisons are possible in the minnesong repertory, since most of the songs survive in only one manuscript. However, for a comparison of two versions of a minnesong, see pp. 114–15.

The first version of Gace Brulé's song (Paris, B.N. fr. 846, f. 41) given here is particularly interesting since the notation is mensural, clearly indicating that the song is in dactylic mode. It is one of the pieces of evidence for the application of the modal theory to other secular monophonic music.

Though both are at different pitch levels, the tonal effect of both versions of the song is Ionian mode (major).

I Fancied I Could Lighten Grief by Singing
(*Mit sange wânde ich mîne sorge krenken*)

The best of this song lies in Fenis' skillful use of the moth-flame symbol, a symbol employed by Goethe in his poem "Sagt es niemand, nur den Weisen." Fenis doubtless obtained it from Folquet's song "Sitot me soi a tart aperceubutz."

[6]Gennrich, *Troubadours, Trouvères, Minnesang and Meistergesang*, p. 48.

De bone amor et de loiaul amie
Minne gebiutet mir daz ich singe

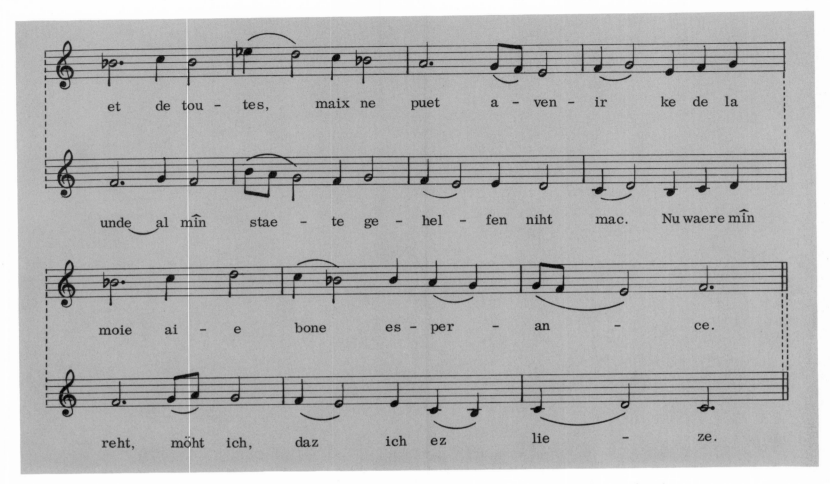

Two versions of Gace Brulé, "De bone amor et de loiaul amie," with contrafact by Rudolf von Fenis adapted to the second version.
Top line, Paris, B.N. fr. 846, f. 41; bottom line, Paris, B.N., n.a. fr. 1050, f. 29.

Mit sange wânde ich mîne sorge krenken

Mit san - ge wân-de ich mî - ne sor - ge kren - ken.
so ich ie mê sin - ge ich ir ie baz ge - den - ke

da - rum - be singe ich de ich si wol - te lân:
sô mugens mit san - ge leid - er niht zer - gân:

wan Min - ne hât mich brâht in sol - hen wân dem

ich sô lîh - te niht en - mac ent - wen - ken,

wan ich im lan - ge her ge - vol - get hân.

Contrafact of "Tant m'ait moneit force de signoraige," Gace Brulé.

Transcription based on critical text of the notes in István Frank and Wendelin Müller-Blatteau, *Trouvères und Minnesänger,* II (West-Ost-Verlag, Saarbrücken, 1956), 78. Manuscript sources on which the critical text are based include: Paris, Arsenal 5198, f. 81; Paris, B.N. fr. 765, f. 57; Paris, B.N. fr. 846, f. 30; Paris, B.N., n.a. fr. 1050, f. 60; Paris, B.N. fr. 844, f. 24; and Paris, B.N. fr. 846, f. 134.

I fancied I could lighten grief by singing,
so now I sing to free my heart from care,
but with the music grievous thoughts come winging
and song can only lay my sorrow bare.
For Lady Love has caught me in her snare,
she gives the hope to which I've long been clinging
and I cannot escape her anywhere.

Since Love in such a manner would reward me,
that I should carry in my heart's recess
the one who can for pain delight afford me,
I'd be a fool should I not acquiesce.
But I shall let Love know of my distress,
for she who's acted so disdainful toward me
could lead me to the house of Happiness.

I wonder at my constant adoration
and how she holds me when I'm far away,
for then I think, this is my consolation,
the sight of her my pain would soon allay.
"Were I with her!" it comforts me to say,
and hope at last to win her admiration,
but soon the hope increases my dismay.

When I'm with her I suffer more than ever,
like one who crowds too closely to a fire
and burns himself as pain for his endeavor,
her beauty pains me, yet it draws me nigher.
When I'm with her I feel my life expire,
but I would die indeed if we should sever,
for she is all my joy and my desire.

I feel the danger in those eyes so tender,
they charm me as the moth is charmed by light
and swiftly flies to perish in its splendor;
her beauty thus deludes my mind and sight.
My foolish heart has brought me to this plight
and, like the moth, is drawn in full surrender
toward flames which shall forever end its flight.

This sprightly tune is transcribed in the first rhythmic mode. It seems to have a light and frivolous character belying the seriousness of the lover's complaint. This cheerful character has led the transcriber to adopt 6/8 time for the transcription to suggest a more light-hearted interpretation to the performer. It is interesting to note that the musical form reflects the rhyme scheme by the use of the same ornamental pattern on the rhyming syllable of the first, third, and sixth lines of the stanza. It should be noted that this detail of construction was used to fit a pre-existent tune.

The Classical Minnesong

Hartmann von Aue

HARTMANN VON AUE was a propertyless knight in the service of the Lords of Aue, whose lands were near Rottenburg in Swabia. He was born between 1160 and 1170 and is mentioned in a song of the year 1220 as having already died. Hartmann was highly regarded by his fellow singers, but less for his minnesongs than for his long narrative poems. These include two Arthurian romances, *Erec* and *Iwein,* both modeled after works by Chrétien de Troyes; *Gregorius,* a legend of St. Gregory, for which Hartmann used a French and possibly also a Latin source; and *Poor Henry,* a didactic narrative, perhaps based on a family tradition of his liege lords.

Sixty of Hartmann's stanzas are extant. Of these, fifty deal with courtly love and the remainder are *Sprüche.* According to one of Hartmann's contemporaries, he also composed at least one *Leich,* but this has been lost. All of Hartmann's songs are characterized by simplicity and gracefulness, but his didactic verse is generally much superior to his minnesongs. The latter were probably composed when Hartmann was quite young, when he was strongly influenced by Romance song and concepts. Then, too, Hartmann was no lover. His was a quiet, unimpassioned character with a tendency toward serious contemplation, and, as a result, his love songs sometimes are little more than mere reflections about the nature of courtly love. The didactic verse is not only more mature and original, but is also more spontaneous. Here the singer is not just following a tradition, but is giving expression to matters with which he is personally and deeply concerned.

No One Is a Happy Man
(*Niemen ist ein saelic man*)

Although this song follows the tradition of the lover's plaint, Hartmann, characteristically enough, almost forgets to mention the lady who supposedly inspired the verses. It has been suggested that Hartmann composed the lines shortly before his departure on a crusade.

No one is a happy man
upon this earth save he alone
who cherishes no secret plan

Ich muoz von rehte den tac iemer minnen

Contrafact of "Ire d'amors ke en mon cuer repaire," Gace Brulé. Source of melody, Paris, B.N., Ms. fr. 846, *Manuscrit Cangé*, f. 61.

and seeks to make no joy his own.
Whose heart is free of longing care
which brings to many death's despair,
who gained what to their heart was dear
and lived to see their treasures go.
To whom that life comes not so near
which I with sorrow learned to know,
for such has been my loss and woe.

It is a cheerless fate, which lends
its greeting to my every pain,
that I must always part from friends
with whom I gladly would remain.
My griefs from my devotion spring
but to the soul no profit bring,
else I should have a better pay
than to lament the constancy
which offers nothing but dismay
for her I never more shall see
who once so loved and cared for me.

I Always Shall Cherish the Day of All Days
(Ich muoz von rehte den tac iemer minnen)

In contrast to most of Hartmann's love songs, this one is happy, even exuberant. The dactylic rhythm is produced by his use of a French melody, which was composed for a ten-syllable line, for a tetrameter poem.

I always shall cherish the day of all days
when first I met her whose charm I extoll:
the loveliest manner and feminine ways.
I'm glad that I gave her my heart and my soul.
This cannot harm her and does me much good,
now I know God and the world as I should.
Since through her virtue my errors shall cease,
I hope that through her all my joys will increase.

I parted from her, and before I could tell
the lady how greatly my passion had grown.
Later a wonderful hour befell
as I discovered her walking alone.
When fate had led me to her I admire
and I had told her my fondest desire,

she was so kind—may God grant her renown!
She was and shall be forever my crown.

Although my body may sometimes take leave,
my heart and my longing must linger with her.
She may bring sadness and cause me to grieve,
yet drive from my heart all the troubles that stir;
from her I've my pleasure as well as my pain,
what she desires of me, she shall obtain.
When I am happy, it's due to her care;
God keep her honor, and her, is my prayer.

The poetry clearly shows the Romance influence in its use of dactyls, and the music has therefore been transcribed in dactylic mode, using the ♩. ♪ ♩ rhythmic interpretation of the poetic foot.

The form of the song is what Gennrich calls a *Rundkanzone* (rounded *chanson*), in which the last phrase of the *Stollen* melody appears again at the end of the *Abgesang*. The minnesingers became especially fond of musical designs in which all or part of the *Stollen* reappeared again at the end and used this principle with many ingenious variations. Gennrich has labeled the design in which the whole *Stollen* melody is repeated at the end of the *Abgesang* a *Reduzierter Strophenlai* (reduced strophic *lai*). It seems likely, however, that the minnesingers would not have considered this form to be related to or derived from the *lai, Leich,* or sequence forms. The present authors prefer to regard both types as variations of a single principle, and to use the term "*Barform* with return" to describe songs using this device.

Gace Brulé's tune has the form AB AB′ CDEB″. The ornamentation of the repeated B sections suggests embellishments which the singer might have added for the repetitions. It is also possible that these varied recurrences were prescribed by the composer or added by the collector.

The Cross Demands a Guileless Mind
(Dem kriuze zimt wol reiner muot)

Hartmann took part in the crusade of 1197, which was led by Leopold of Austria, and may also have participated in the previous crusade, that of 1189. The last stanza of the song is a tribute to his departed liege lord.

The cross demands a guileless mind
and chaste behavior:
so may salvation be combined
with worldly favor.
And it is not a little chain
for men as we
who o'er their bodies cannot gain
the mastery.
It wants not that one shirks
beneath it righteous works;
though wrought on coat of mail
within the heart it must prevail.

Then, knights, repay that which is due
and join the strife
for one whose love has given you
both wealth and life.
Who e'er for honor raised a sword
or for a prize
and now denies it to his Lord,
he is not wise.
For he whom fate shall bless
and grant his tour success
shall have a double claim:
to heaven's grace and worldly fame.

The world deceptively has smiled,
has beckoned me,
and I pursued her, as a child,
so foolishly.
I followed her with eager feet,
the wanton fair;
where none has found a safe retreat,

I hastened there.
Now save me, Jesus Christ,
from that which would entice,
from him who would ensnare,
through this your sign which now I bear.

Since death has torn away from me
my patron lord,
the world, however fair it be,
brings no reward.
So few of all my joys remain:
he took the rest,
to labor for the spirit's gain
is now the best.
And may he share the grace
I strive for in his place,
I grant him half, and more,
and pray we meet at heaven's door.

The Wife Who Sends Her Cherished Lord
(*Swelch vrowe sendet lieben man*)

This song is unique among all the German crusade songs in that it pays tribute to the wives who remain behind and support their husbands with their prayers.

The wife who sends her cherished lord
with cheerful heart upon this quest
shall purchase half of his reward,
if she at home but do her best
that all her virtue may declare.
She here shall pray to God for both
and he for both shall battle there.

Heinrich von Morungen

HEINRICH VON MORUNGEN was born in northern Thuringia about the year 1150, probably spent much of his life at the court at Mainz, and died in Leipzig in 1222. He was a poet of great originality and imagination and, as a singer of love songs, was unequaled even by Walther von der Vogelweide. It is quite possible that Morungen became acquainted with Hausen in Mainz and that he was influenced by the older poet. Like Hausen, he was familiar with Provençal song and with the Romance code of courtly love, but in his hands the fixed conventions and stereotyped situations of the troubadours took on an immediacy and vitality which makes them live, even for the twentieth-century reader. Although Morungen accepts the abstraction of courtly love, he does not stray far from the real world about him, and there is always something very personal and human in his lovers' laments. Above all, however, it is the richness and originality of his imagery which make Morungen's verse distinctive.

In matters of structure Morungen has the true poet's talent for joining form and content. His metrical patterns are more complex than those of Dietmar and Kürenberg, but they are smooth, pliable, and lyrical. There is no straining for effect, and he never descends to a mere tour de force of rhyme, as did Hausen and Veldeke at times. His stanzaic verse shows an advance over that of his predecessors, in that the individual strophes are not just variations of the same theme, but show relationship and continuity.

In addition to being well acquainted with Romance song, Morungen was probably familiar with some classical literature, especially that of Ovid, and with medieval Latin verse. He was apparently little known in his day and, unlike his two chief rivals, Walther and Neidhart, exerted little, if any, influence on the later minnesingers. Thirty-eight of his poems are extant.

Oh! Oh! Will Nevermore the Glow
(Owê, sol aber mir iemer me)

In this dawn song, which is also an alternating song, the knight and lady are far apart and are recalling in alternate monologues the ecstasy and sorrow of parting.

The first two stanzas describe the same situation as seen first by the knight, then by the lady; the second two stanzas are similarly parallel to each other. All four stanzas, however, are linked by simple but effective devices. The refrain at the end of the first stanza leads up to the "daybreak" of the second stanza, the "lay" at the end of the second stanza to the "slept" at the beginning of the third stanza, etc. The original is one of the most beautiful love songs of European literature.

> "Oh! Oh!
> Will nevermore the glow
> of that fair form as white
> as newly-fallen snow
> come to me through the night?
> The sight deceived my eyes,
> I thought I saw arise
> the bright moon in the skies.
>   Then came the dawn!"

> "Oh! Oh!
> And will he never know
> the daybreak here again,
> nor watch the darkness go,
> nor share my sorrow when
> I cry: 'Alas, it's day!'?
> That he, too, used to say
> when he beside me lay.
>   Then came the dawn!"

> "Oh! Oh!
> A thousand times, it seems
> she kissed me as I slept,
> and, till I left my dreams,
> how bitterly she wept.
> But then I knew how best
> to put her tears to rest;
> she drew me to her breast.
>   Then came the dawn!"

> "Oh! Oh!
> So many times has he
> seen more than was his due
> and quite uncovered me;

> he wanted just to view
> poor me, all bare and bright.
> I wondered that my knight
> so much enjoyed the sight.
>   Then came the dawn!"

What Lady Is She
(Sach ieman die vrouwen)

In most of the great number of lover's laments which the minnesingers produced, a clever playing with sentiment is apparent. In those of Morungen, however, the emotion is stronger and seems more genuine, sometimes almost violent. The primitive Germanic lust for revenge shows through the courtly façade in the last lines of this poem, where the singer proposes to expose the cruelty of the lady. The stanzas are not directly continuous in time, but represent separate stages of an unhappy love affair.

> What lady is she
> whom one may see
> in the window there?
> Her beautiful face
> and airy grace
> can free me from care,
> for she glows with the warmth of the rising sun
> in the morning's early light.
> Long was she hidden from sight
> and dark was the night,
> but now the world is all fair.

> If someone is here
> whose reason is clear
> in this hour of gloom,
> seek her who bereft me
> of beauty and left me
> to sorrow and doom,
> and entreat her to hasten and sooth my grief
> while life and breath remain.
> For torments of passion and pain
> I cannot restrain
> are driving me to the tomb.

Then clearly make known
my fate on the stone
that covers my grave.
Tell of beauty adored
and a lover ignored,
that the knight or the knave
as he passes may learn from my sombre tale
of love that burns and rends.
There may he read how she sends
cold death to her friends,
so cruelly does she behave.

Oh Sweet, Benevolent Assassin
(*Vil sûze senfte tôterinne*)

The idea of a love so strong that its bonds cannot be broken in this life is a basic concept of courtly love. However, the minnesingers, for all their idealization of love, were oriented essentially to matters of this world. Only from Morungen do we learn of bonds of love so strong that even death cannot break them.

Oh sweet, benevolent assassin,
why slay your love and me and cast aside
the hopes and tender ties that fasten
our hearts, and just to please your woman's pride?
Oh can you dream that, having killed me,
you then will wander free of my design?
No, no, so full your love has filled me
that evermore your soul is wed to mine.
Though here my heart may suffer sorrow
from one who lies so near it,
I tell you, soon, perhaps tomorrow,
my soul will love and serve you there,
a light and laughing spirit.

On Such a Cloud of Joy as This
(*In sô hôher swebender wunne*)

Early Germanic poetry had no rhyme, and depended for its lyrical quality on two devices: regular rhythm and regular alliteration. With the coming of rhyme, alliteration became less important, but it did not disappear. Morungen's irregular but very effective use of alliteration is the source of much of the lyrical quality of such songs as this.

On such a cloud of joy as this
my soul has never sailed so high before.
I hover as on wings of bliss
with thoughts of only her whom I adore,
because her love unlocked the door
which leads into my inmost heart
and entered there for evermore.

All other raptures that remain
with this great happiness cannot compare.
Let earth and sky and wood and plain
with me a time of soaring gladness share.
For, filled with hope and freed from care,
and thrilled by dreams of ecstasy,
my joy is more than I can bear.

What all-entrancing words were those
which sounded, oh so sweetly, in my ear!
And what a gentle pain arose
to sink with joy into my bosom here,
where such delights did then appear,
such loving overcame me so,
that from my eye there fell a tear.

How happy was that sweet event!
How blissful was that hour, the fading night,
when lovely lips gave their consent
and spoke the word which made my heart so light
that I must tremble as in fright.
And even now love's power is so,
I know not how to praise her right.

Long I Brooded, Lost in Thought
(*Lanc bin ich geweset verdâht*)

The music to all of the songs which appear under Morungen's name in the manuscripts has been lost. This text, however, which is ascribed to a "Her Morunk," is probably also by him and is a contrafact for which the music is extant. The text is somewhat inferior to those of

Lanc bin ich geweset verdâht

Contrafact of "Je ne sui pais ebahis," anonymous trouvère.

Transcription based on critical text of the notes in István Frank and Wendelin Müller-Blatteau, *Trouvères und Minnesänger,* II (West-Ost-Verlag, Saarbrücken, 1956), 109. Manuscript sources on which the critical text are based are: Paris, B.N. fr. 846, f. 89; Paris, B.N. fr. 1591, f. 97; and Paris, B.N. fr. 24406, f. 56.

Morungen's other love songs, but this may be due to inaccuracies arising from oral transmission.

Long I brooded, lost in thought,
sad, unloved I long have been,
then to me the news was brought
which rejoiced my heart within.
Comfort I should win
from this lady of mine;
how could I now longer pine?
When her lips requite
my love with such delight
I can sorrow never more:
all my grief is o'er.

The secular songs of troubadours, trouvères, and minnesingers frequently used the modern major and minor scales (Ionian and Aeolian modes), which, although not explicitly recognized by theorists until Glareanus' *Dodekachordon* (1547), were actually used much earlier. Johannes de Grocheo and Anonymous II, however, did intimate that secular monody was not restricted to the church modes, although they did not describe what was used instead. The melody of this song is one of those in major, which gives it a very modern sound in places.

The melody of the last part of the *Abgesang* is repeated at the end of the song, so that the form is:

AB	AB	CDEF	DEF
Stollen	*Stollen*	*Abgesang*	

Wolfram von Eschenbach

WOLFRAM VON ESCHENBACH was born about the year 1170 at Eschenbach in northeastern Bavaria. Although his family belonged to the nobility, they were poor, being *Ministeriale,* who administered estates belonging to the Counts of Oettingen. From about 1203 until his death, Wolfram lived principally at the court of Hermann of Thuringia. Today he is known primarily for his epic poetry: *Titurel, Willehalm,* and particularly the great masterpiece of the German Middle Ages, *Parzival.* In the thirteenth century, however, Wolfram's fame rested equally on his minnesongs, of which, unfortunately, only eight have survived. He was perhaps the most profound and versatile poet of his time, but his peculiar, acrid humor, his play with strange pictures and symbols, and his abruptness of expression made for a difficult style, to which one of his contemporaries, Gottfried von Strassburg, strongly objected. Even his lyric poetry occasionally has a darkness and obscurity, which, however, is often animated by a spirited sensuousness. Perhaps because he came from the lowest stratum of nobility Wolfram reflects in his verse more earthy vigor and less conventional manners than most of the minnesingers. In one of his poems he is so unconventional as to praise the happiness of marriage and contrast its joys with the transitory pleasure of extramarital love.

Dawn Strikes Its Claws
(*Sine klâwen*)

Apparently Wolfram particularly liked the dawn song, since five of his surviving songs are of that type. This song consists of a dialogue between a lady and a watchman, whose opening words present the most striking and powerful metaphor in minnesong literature.

"Dawn strikes its claws
 through massive clouds and mounts in flight.
It rises with relentless power
and with it draws
the graying shadows of the night.
I see the day, which at this hour
will steal the pleasure of the man
whom I admitted fearfully.

Do man dem edelen syn getzelt

• Jena, Universitätsbibliothek, Jenaer Liederhandschrift, f. 128.

*The *b* is found in the first *Stollen* only.

**The up-beat *a* is missing in the second *Stollen*.

The small notes indicate those to be used for the repeat of the *Stollen*.

I'll get him out now, if I can:
his stately bearing must have blinded me."

"The song you sing,
oh watchman, takes my joy away
and makes more grievous my lament.
The news you bring
each morning at the break of day
gives only sorrow and discontent.
Such words I do not care to hear,
so hold your tongue and let us be,
and I'll reward you, never fear,
if my dear love remains awhile with me."

"He still must go
sweet lady, say goodbye, that he
may leave as promptly as he came,
and later show
his love for you more stealthily,
preserve his life and his good name.
He trusted in my faithfulness
to get him safely forth from here;
the night has passed when your caress
and kisses bought my aid to bring him near."

"Sing what you will,
oh watchman, sing, but let him stay,
who brought his love and here found mine.
Your rough words fill
us always with intense dismay.
Before the morning star can shine
upon this knight who visits me,
while still no rays of sunlight part
the night, you make him rise and flee
from my bare arms, but never from my heart."

But still the clear
bright rays the sun cast overhead
and the warning watchman's rude request
caused her to fear
for the gallant knight who shared her bed:
she pressed him closely to her breast.
And yet the knight was strong and brave,
despite the watchman's song above;

their warm and tender parting gave
them kisses (and much more) as spoils of love.

The Tent of Hermann Then Was Placed
(*Do man dem edelen syn getzelt*)

This song is a part of the *Wartburg Singers' War,* a collection of songs describing a contest at the court of Hermann of Thuringia between the legendary minnesinger, Heinrich von Ofterdingen, on the one side, and Walther von der Vogelweide and a minnesinger known as "The Virtuous Scribe" on the other. The singing contest is conducted like a tournament with Reinmar von Zweter and Wolfram von Eschenbach as marshal and judge. The song below, which appears under the name of Wolfram, introduces a peddler who appears before Count Hermann with riddles for sale which the singers are to attempt to solve. The author or authors of the lyrics of the *Wartburg Singers' War* are unknown, but it is quite possible that many of the melodies used were actually composed by the minnesingers who appear in the work.

> The tent of Hermann then was placed
> upon a field by which a river's waters raced.
> Then came a peddler whom I greatly praise.
> He had a cloth of baldaquin
> to shield his wares. I wonder what may be within?
> (The wise man hid beneath it from our gaze.)
> "Come all who want to buy from me.
> I have a frightful beast thereunder
> that never eye shall see again,
> nor ever yet has seen." The kindly prince spoke
>   then:
> "Whate'er the price, I'll buy it for a wonder."

This song is an example of a *Barform* with return, in which the complete *Stollen* melody is reused at the end of the *Abgesang.* The repeats are literal, with the same ornamentation each time, except for the slight modification at the end of the first line of the second *Stollen.*

Many of the melismas of this song use either five or seven notes. Although they are transcribed with even rhythmic values, they were probably performed as

Jamer ist mir entsprungen

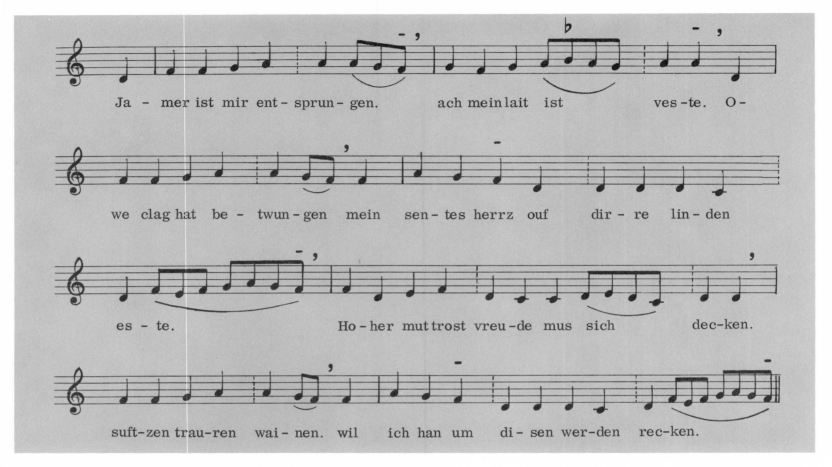

Ja – mer ist mir ent – sprun – gen. ach mein lait ist ves –te. O-

we clag hat be – twun – gen mein sen – tes herrz ouf dir – re lin – den

es – te. Ho – her mut trost vreu – de mus sich dec – ken.

suft – zen trau – ren wai – nen. wil ich han um di – sen wer – den rec – ken.

Vienna, Nationalbibliothek, Titurel Hs. 40 (Ambr. 421).

characteristic ornament groups, with the first or last note of the pattern (in every case the same note) treated as the principal note of the group. Melismatic songs of this type might also be sung in some type of free rhythm with good effect.

Grief as a River Rushes
(*Jamer ist mir entsprungen*)

This song is one of the many which make up Wolfram's *Titurel,* a fragmentary Arthurian romance which was perhaps intended as an interlude in *Parzival. Titurel* is unique in Middle High German literature in that it is a long narrative poem which employs a lyric rather than an epic form. All of the stanzas have the same *Ton,* and all were intended to be sung to the same melody, that which appears here. Sigune, the heroine, sings of her lover, Schianatulander.

Grief as a river rushes,
pain I cannot still
overwhelms me and crushes
my longing heart upon this pleasant hill.
Comfort, peace, and happiness take flight;
sighs and tears and sorrow
shall I have because of this fair knight.

Very little is known about the music used to accompany the epic poetry of the Middle Ages. No music has survived for Middle High German verse using the standard epic form. In French sources, a little phrase in Adam de la Halle's pastoral, *Le Jeu de Robin et Marion* (c. 1284), is set to the text of a line from a *chanson de geste* (the French epic form) and is believed to be the melody to which it was originally sung. French epics were chanted by repeating the same melodic formula for the group of lines forming a thought unit, with the last line using a different, closing formula. Each such section, which might contain any number of lines, was called a *laisse.*

Though German epics did not use the *laisse* structure of the *chanson de geste,* they were probably sung to similar repetitive formulas which could be remembered easily and which were not so much melodies as motives which could be combined and adapted to the line. The German poets make a distinction between the verbs *sagen* (to say) and *singen* (to sing), and speak of minstrels as doing both in their performances (see p. 155). The German term for "epic," *Sage,* suggests that the method of performance indicated by the word *sagen* was not simply "speaking" but intoned recitation or chanting, probably with formulas similar to the psalm tones.

The survival of this particular song is probably due to the fact that *Titurel* does not employ epic form, so that the compiler of the manuscript felt obliged to provide a sample of music for the lyric form. For *Parzival* itself, on the other hand, such conventional patterns must have been used by the singer that it was considered unnecessary to write them down.

The form of this song is a lyric form, A B A C D A C. It is interesting to note that it is in Hypolydian mode (the plagal modes are seldom used in minnesongs). The transcription is in free rhythm.

Eight songs with melodies (*Weisen*) or *Töne* ascribed to Wolfram appear in meistersinger manuscripts, but their structure is so different from any of the surviving poems of the minnesinger that it is impossible to reconstruct music which would fit any of them from these sources. Wolfram was considered by the meistersingers to be one of the twelve first Great Masters of their guild tradition. To be considered a Master, each singer had to be able to compose in the various *Töne* attributed to the twelve founders. Probably all the songs labeled as *Töne* of Wolfram originated in this manner. Two of the tunes are called *Weisen* and may actually have been considered by the meistersingers to be genuine melodies by Wolfram, but, if so, they were so extensively altered by oral transmission and by the application of the meistersingers' rules that it is impossible to reconstruct their original form.

Walther von der Vogelweide

Iᴺ ᴛʜᴇ ᴠᴇʀꜱᴇ of Walther von der Vogelweide the minne-song reached the height of its glory. In it all the various tendencies of the genre were brought together by a singer who combined acuteness of perception, an almost complete mastery of the spoken word, and a sensitive spirit which could express an endless scale of human emotions. Little is known of the poet's life. He was born in the Tyrol about 1170 of noble but obscure parents and, after having learned his art in Vienna, spent most of his life wandering from court to court, earning his livelihood with songs. In 1220 Friedrich II granted him a small feudal estate, probably near Würzburg, where he died about 1228. He is said to be buried in the Cathedral of Würzburg.

Walther's chief contribution to the lyric poetry of his day was the raising of didactic and political songs to a high level of literature. Through such verses he became the social critic of his time and an influential propagandist for a strong empire. Because of his attacks on the papacy, he has been called a forerunner of Martin Luther, a designation which fits only in part, for Walther's opposition to the papacy was based only on political grounds.

In Walther's love songs and nature songs the natural freshness and naiveté of Dietmar and Kürenberg appear in metrical forms which reveal all of the ingenuity of the Provençal troubadours. Here his wayward mood vacillates between half-concealed merriment and mild melancholy. The prevailing temper of the social and political songs is one of dark brooding which often breaks forth in violence and venom.

Now Has the Winter Brought Harm to Us All
(*Uns hat der winter geschat über al*)

The dactylic rhythm of this poem and the repeated rhyme both place it in Walther's early period, a time when he was strongly influenced by Romance song and had not yet developed a characteristic style of his own.

> Now has the winter brought harm to us all,
> meadow and forest are both in its thrall,
> where many voices still sang in the fall.
> If I were watching the maidens play ball,
> soon I'd be hearing the forest birds call.

Uns hat der winter geschat über al

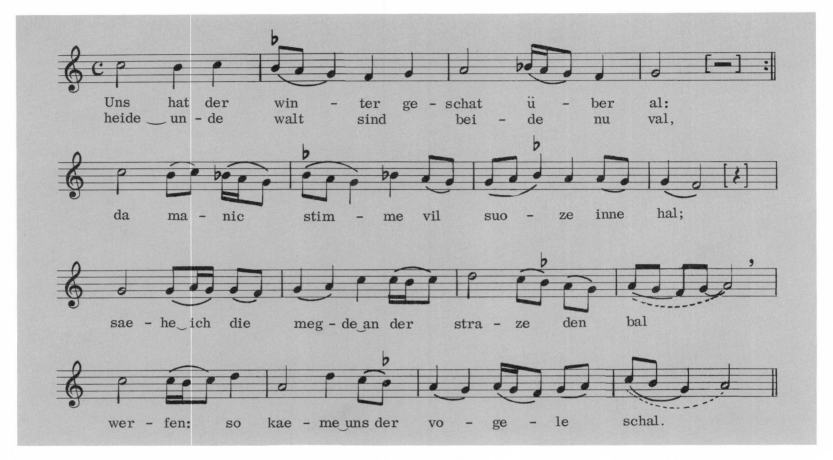

Uns hat der win - ter ge - schat ü - ber al:
heide un - de walt sind bei - de nu val,
da ma - nic stim - me vil suo - ze inne hal;
sae - he ich die meg - de an der stra - ze den bal
wer - fen: so kae - me uns der vo - ge - le schal.

Contrafact of "Quant voi les prés flourir et blanchoier," Monios (probably Moniot d'Arras or Moniot de Paris).
Source of melody, Paris, B.N., Fonds fr. 844, *Manuscrit du Roi*, f. 121.

Could I but slumber the whole winter long!
When I'm not sleeping he does me much wrong,
great is his might and his malice is strong,
yet is he conquered when May sings its song.
Where frost now glistens shall flowers then throng.

This is one of four songs which Gennrich considers to be contrafacts of Romance models.[1] In this transcription, the dactylic rhythm of the poetry has been noted in duple meter, making the basic rhythmic pattern ♩ ♩ ♩. This rhythmic possibility was admitted by Beck in his later theories.[2]

Blissfully He Lay
(*Friuntlîchen lac*)

Although approximately 188 songs and *Sprüche* of Walther are extant (the number depending on the grouping of the stanzas), we have only a single dawn song from

[1]The others are: "Fro welt, ir sult dem wirte sagen" (melody of Blondel de Nesle, "Onques nus hom ne chanta"); "Muget ir schouwen waz dem meien" (melody of Gautier d'Espinal, "Quant je voi l'erbe menue"); "Wol mich der stunde, das ich sie erkunde" (melody of Bernart de Ventadorn, "Can vei la flor, l'erba e la folha"). See Friedrich Gennrich, "Melodien Walthers von der Vogelweide," *Zeitschrift für deutsches Altertum*, LXXIX (1942), 45–47.

[2]Beck, *Le chansonnier Cangé.*

Friuntlîchen lac

Friunt-lî-chen lac ein rî-ter vil ge-meit an ei-ner frou-wen ar-me. Er kôs den mor-gen lieht, do er in dur diu wol-ken so ver-re schî-nen sach. Diu frou-we in lei-de sprach: "we ge-sche-he dir tac, daz du mich lâst bî lie-be lan-ger blî-ben nieht: daz si da hei-zent min-ne deis nie-wan se-ne-de leit."

Source of melody, "Walthers Guldin Wyse," Munich, Staatsbibliothek, Cod. germ. 4997, f. 736 (the Colmar manuscript).

*The meistersinger text has two more syllables with two more *c*'s here.

**The manuscript has two *e*'s here.

***The last phrase was a cadence embellishment on only one syllable in the meistersinger version:

him. Considering the general popularity of the type, this fact is at first somewhat surprising. However, when one considers that the dawn song had become conventional and very inflexible in form before Walther began to compose, one can understand why an imaginative artist would avoid it. In this song Walther adds nothing new to the conventional dawn song. He does, however, make it more animated by presenting the plaints of both lovers in each stanza, rather than in alternating stanzas. Certain of Walther's rhymes show this to be one of his earliest songs.

Blissfully he lay,
the lusty cavalier,
upon a lady's arm.   He saw the morning light
as, gleaming from a distance,   through the mist it broke.
With grief the lady spoke,
"I wish you woe, oh Day,
 for I can stay no longer   with my handsome knight.
What's known as love is only   a longing and a fear."

"Lady, I implore
you not to sorrow so.
It's better for us both   that I should now depart,
I see the silver gleam   of the morning star above."
"Oh stay with me, my love,
and let us speak no more
of leaving, that you may   not so distress my heart.
Indeed, it is not right.   Why need you haste to go?"

"Lady, it shall be,
I'll stay a while with you.
Now tell me what you wish,   but still it must be brief,
that we may now deceive   the watchers once again."
"My heart is filled with pain.
Before I shall be free
to lie with you once more   I'll have so much of grief.
Don't stay away too long!   Such nights are all too few."

"I'll come whene'er I may,
so do not be forlorn.
Though I must now depart   and leave you for a while,
my heart shall still remain   and shall not stir from here."
"Obey me now, my dear;
you will not stay away
if you are true to me   without deceit or guile.
Alas, the night is gone.   I see the breaking morn."

"Lady, I must fly!
Permit me now to ride
away from here, to save   your name must I take leave.
So loud and near the watchman   sings his morning song."
"He will be here ere long,
so we must say goodbye,
but how this sad departure   causes me to grieve!
May God in heaven be   your guardian and your guide!"

The lover soon was gone,
and all his joy had flown.
He left the pretty lady   weeping bitter tears.
But he was always loyal   because he shared her bed.
"Whene'er I hear," she said,
a melody at dawn,
my heart shall always be   distressed with pain and fears.
A sad and longing woman   I lie here now alone."

The "Guldin Wyse" ascribed to Walther in the Colmar manuscript has been fitted to two of Walther's poems by Bützler and Gennrich.[3] The form of the meistersinger version of the tune is a *Barform* with a return of the complete *Stollen* melody at the end of the *Abgesang*, the type of *Barform* most favored by the meistersingers. A long ornament replaces the last note of the repeated *Stollen* melody

[3]"Friuntlîchen lac" in Gennrich, *Mittelhochdeutsche Liedkunst*, p. 12; "Maneger klaget die schoenen zıt" in Carl Bützler, *Untersuchungen zu den Melodien Walthers von der Vogelweide* (Jena, Deutsche Arbeiten der Universität Köln, Nr. 12, 1940), p. 62.

at the end. The meistersingers loved to add embellishments of this sort (*Blumen*), particularly at the beginning and end of their songs. In the various reconstructions of the "Guldin Wyse," however, this vocal melisma must be fitted to the last line of Walther's text in syllabic style in order to have enough music to fit the poem.

When adapting meistersinger tunes to fit minnesinger texts, it is also usually impossible to preserve the same ligatures as those fitted to the meistersingers' texts. The slurs shown for "Friuntlîchen lac," "Ich saz ûf eime steine," and "Mir hat her Gerhart Atze ein pfert" are those necessary for the reconstruction and do not follow exactly the groupings in the meistersinger manuscripts.

Under the Linden
(*Under der linden*)

Medieval German society was very class-conscious, and the minnesingers in their love songs made a definite distinction between the courtly love of knights and ladies, with all its traditional etiquette, and the simple, natural love of man and woman. Although Walther usually sang of courtly love, he once declared that "woman" was a more complimentary term than "lady," that femininity was preferable to lofty pride. The naively charming peasant girl who here describes a meeting with her lover well supports his claim.

> Under the linden
> I and my lover
> softly were bedded in grass and shade.
> And if you should wander
> there, you'll discover
> many a broken bloom and blade.
> By the forest, in the dale,
> "tandaradei!"
> sweetly sang the nightingale.
>
> I went to our meeting
> and did not tarry,
> for he I loved had gone before.
> Oh, what a greeting!
> Holy Mary,

> I'll be blessed for evermore!
> Did he kiss me? Yes, and how!
> "Tandaradei."
> See how red my lips are now.
>
> My lover had laid
> with care meanwhile
> a lovely bed of flowers for me.
> The village maid
> will slyly smile
> who walks there past the linden tree
> and sees the spot where on that day
> "tandaradei"
> my head among the roses lay.
>
> If anyone guesses
> that we were together
> (May God forbid!), I'd surely die.
> Of his caresses,
> hid by the heather,
> may no one know but he and I
> and the bird that sang so well:
> "tandaradei."
> I can trust it not to tell.

How Beautiful Her Form and Face
(*Si wunderwol gemachet wîp*)

Walther's technique of enumerating the separate beauties of his beloved is quite similar to that employed by the author of several of the Songs of Solomon, who, indeed, may have inspired this song.

> How beautiful her form and face,
> may she give thanks to me ere long,
> for both of them I now shall place
> with loving care within my song.
> I serve the ladies, one and all,
> but I have chosen her alone.
> To other men may others fall,
> I care not how they praise their own,
> though they use song and air
> that I composed; as I praise here, may they praise
>   there.

Si wunderwol gemachet wîp

Kremsmünster, Stiftsbibliothek, Ms. 127, f. 130.

Her head is so exceeding fair
as only heaven e'er may be,
with it can nothing else compare
in splendor truly heavenly.
Two stars are there and gleaming clear,
I'd like to see myself therein,
would she but hold those stars so near,
then might a miracle begin,

to make me young once more
and bring delight to him whose heart with love is
    sore.

God made her cheeks a true delight
in which his richest color glows,
the deepest red, the purest white,
here, like a lily, there, a rose.

I hope it's not a sin to say
I'd rather watch her blushes than
admire the starry Milky Way,
but why should I, oh foolish man,
place her so high above me?
My praise would cause me pain, were she too
    proud to love me.

Such lips she has, so full and red,
if I could bring them close to mine
I would arise as from the dead
and nevermore would faint or pine.
Whose cheek she touches with those lips
would gladly have them stay for hours,
for from them such a fragrance drips
as balsam or perfume of flowers.
If she would lend a kiss
I'd give it back whene'er she wished, be sure of this.

Her throat, her hands, her feet I've seen
and found how greatly all excelled,
and should I praise what lies between,
I'd but relate what I beheld.
I must confess, no warning cry
was uttered when I saw her bare.
She saw me not when she let fly
the Cupid's dart which still I wear.
I praise the blissful state
in which the lovely woman left her bath of late.

Only two manuscripts exist containing melodies of Walther's songs, and of the five remaining songs, only the famous crusade song "Nu alrêst leb' ich mir werde" has been preserved complete. Two phrases of the love song "Si wunderwol gemachet wîp" are contained in the Kremsmünster Stiftsbibliothek Ms. 127. Unfortunately even this fragment is lacking the neume for the last syllable of the line, which has been supplied by the transcriber. This is one of the most highly embellished melodies surviving for the whole period. The principle used in the transcription is that of making each syllable of equal length and considering the long melismas ornaments. It would also be possible to use free rhythm in the perform-ance of this song, instead of the more exact note values given in this transcription.

Welcome and with All Good Cheer
(*Ir sult sprechen: 'willekomen'*)

In this first patriotic song of German literature Walther sings of the superior grace and excellence of German society. The line "eastward here as far as Hungary" indicates that the verses were composed on the occasion of Walther's return after a long absence to the Viennese court.

Welcome and with all good cheer
him who brings you stories; I am he.
All the other tales told here
were an empty wind. Now come hear me.
First give me my reward,
if it satisfies,
things I'll tell, perhaps, to open wide your eyes.
See what gifts you can afford!

German ladies shall embrace
news of such a nature that they may
better charm us with their grace.
That I'll do for no excessive pay.
What shall be the fee?
I can't reach so high;
I'll be modest if the ladies be not shy,
and will greet me tenderly.

I have traveled far and wide,
have traversed the best of lands indeed;
may misfortune be my guide,
should I make my erring heart concede
that it was impressed
by their foreign ways.
Well, what would I gain by false and empty praise?
German manners are the best!

From the Elbe to the Rhine,
eastward here as far as Hungary,
there the fairest beauties shine
that this wanderer ever hopes to see.

He who understands
lovely forms as well
as I, would swear, by God, our peasant girls excel
fine ladies in all other lands.

German men are all refined,
angels can't surpass the women here;
who thinks otherwise is blind,
so, at least to me, it would appear.
He who seeks in vain
culture, love, and light,
should come into a land where all of these unite.
May I evermore remain!

Now My Life Has Gained Some Meaning
(*Nu alrêst leb' ich mir werde*)

There are various theories about the time of origin of this crusade song. One scholar maintains that it was written to support the crusade of Friedrich I, in 1189; another that it was written, perhaps in Jerusalem, when Walther was taking part in the crusade of 1219–21; a third believes that it was written while Walther, as an old man, was on the crusade of 1228. However this may be, it was certainly composed as a hymn to be sung by pilgrims and crusaders. One cannot say that Walther was successful as a hymn writer; however, the work is important for the fact that its music is the oldest extant of any significant song by a minnesinger.

Now my life has gained some meaning
since these sinful eyes behold
the sacred land with meadows greening
whose renown is often told.
This was granted me from God:
to see the land, the holy sod,
which in human form He trod.

Splendid lands of wealth and power,
I've seen many, far and near,
yet of all are you the flower.
What a wonder happened here!
That a maid a child should bear,
Lord of all the angels fair,
was not this a wonder rare?

Here was He baptized, the Holy,
that all people might be pure.
Here He died, betrayed and lowly,
that our bonds should not endure.
Else our fate had been severe.
Hail, oh cross, thorns and spear!
Heathens, woe! Your rage is clear.

Then to hell the Son descended
from the grave in which He lay,
by the Father still attended,
and the Spirit whom none may
give a name: in one are three,
an arrowshaft in unity.
This did Abraham once see.

When He there defeated Satan,
ne'er has kaiser battled so,
He returned, our ways to straighten.
Then the Jews had fear and woe:
watch and stone were both in vain,
He appeared in life again,
whom their hands had struck and slain.

To this land, so He has spoken,
shall a fearful judgment come.
Widows' bonds shall then be broken
and the orphans' foe be dumb,
and the poor no longer cower
under sad misuse of power.
Woe to sinners in that hour!

Christians, heathen, Jews, contending,
claim it as a legacy.
May God judge with grace unending
through His blessed Trinity.
Strife is heard on every hand:
ours the only just demand,
He will have us rule the land.

The most famous of all the minnesinger tunes is the one complete song from the Münster manuscript fragment, Walther's crusade song. Many different scholars have transcribed this tune, and three different versions are given here. Arnold Schering transcribes it in duple

Nu alrêst (version A)

Münster, Staatsarchiv, Ms. VII, 51. Fragment, f. 1.

Transcription by Arnold Schering, *Geschichte der Musik in Beispielen* (Leipzig, Breitkopf & Härtel, 1931), p. 6.

Nu alrêst (version B)

Münster fragment.
Transcription by Friedrich Gennrich, "Sieben Melodien zu mittelhochdeutschen Minneliedern," *Zeitschrift für Musikwissenschaft*, VII (1924–25), 98.

meter. Friedrich Gennrich has made several different transcriptions, all according to the modal theory. It is interesting to see the different possibilities which this theory allows by comparing the transcription made in 1924 with his latest edition of the tune in 1960.

· The melody, one of the most beautiful of all minnesinger songs, has many points of similarity with some Latin and Romance songs. Gennrich believes that Walther adapted a melody by the troubadour Jaufre Rudels as a contrafact, but the similarity between the two songs seems

Nu alrêst (version C)

Al - ler - erst lebe ich mir wer - de

Sît mîn sün - dic ou - ge siht

Daz reine lant und ouch die er - de

Der man sô vil ê - ren giht

Mirst ge - schehen des ich ie bat

Ich bin ko - men an die stat

Da got men - nisch - lî - chen trat.

Münster fragment.

Transcription by Friedrich Gennrich, *Troubadours, Trouvères, Minnesang and Meistergesang* (Köln, Arno Volk, 1960), p. 51.

Used by permission of Friedrich Gennrich.

to the present writer to be too slight to make this probable.[4] Huisman shows the strong similarity of this tune to the hymn melody "Te Joseph celebrent," and Abert finds resemblances to it in the Bordesholm Marian lament.[5]

I Sat upon a Stone
(Ich saz ûf eime steine)

In this political song Walther deplores the breakdown of law and order as a result of the imperial interregnum. The absence of peace and justice make impossible the fulfillment of a knight's chief desire, the achieving of wealth, fame, and God's grace. Walther's self-description in the opening lines inspired the well-known painting of him which appears in the Manesse manuscript.

I sat upon a stone,
leg over leg was thrown,
upon my knee an elbow rested
and in my open hand was nested
my chin and half my cheek.
My thoughts were dark and bleak:
I wondered how a man should live,
to this no answer could I give.

Could man three things enjoy
and none the rest destroy?
The two are worldly wealth and fame,
which often bring each other shame;
the third is Heaven's grace,
which takes the highest place.
I wish that I might have all three,
but it, alas, can never be
that one man's heart should hold
both worldly fame and gold
and aught of Heaven's favor, too.
No road will let them through
where treason would betray you
and naked force would slay you.
Peace and right are wounded sore;
the three have no protection till
    the two are well and strong once more.

I Heard a River Flow
(Ich hôrte ein wazzer diezen)

When the German emperor Heinrich VI died in 1197, the political situation in the Empire became critical. Heinrich's son, Friedrich II, was elected emperor, but Pope Innocent III refused to recognize him, and other candidates for the throne appeared. Walther supported Philip of Swabia, who was crowned in 1198. The "wretched kings" mentioned at the end of the poem were the kings of England, France, and Denmark, whom Walther accuses of attempting to gain control of the Empire. Three of Walther's best-known *Sprüche,* including the preceding one, are composed in this *Ton.*

I heard a river flow,
saw bright fish come and go.
I saw the world: all things concealed
in reed and grass, in wood and field
that creep or walk or fly
between the earth and sky.
I saw all this and can relate
that all things live in fearful hate,
that beast and reptile corps
wage unrelenting wars,
and birds with their own kind unite
to carry on a ceaseless fight.
But this I also saw—
the beasts have still their law.
They have their kings and rights
and choose their lords and knights.
But oh you German lands
where no one voice commands,
how can the flies their monarch know
and German honor fall so low!
Unite as oft of old!
The foreign crowns grow bold,

[4]Gennrich, *Troubadours, Trouvères, Minnesang and Meistergesang,* p. 71.
[5]J. A. Huisman, *Neue Wege zur dichterischen und musikalischen Technik Walthers von der Vogelweide* (Utrecht, Domplein, 1950), p. 147; A. Abert, "Das Nachleben des Minnesangs im liturgischen Spiel," *Musikforschung,* I (1948), 104.

Ich saz ûf eime steine

(Instrumental)

Ich saz ûf ei - me stei - ne und
daz kin-ne und ein mîn wan - ge. dô

dâh - te bein mit bei - ne. Dar ûf satzt ich den el - len-
dâh-te ich mir vil an - ge. wie man zer wel - te sol - te

bo - gen, ich hete in mî - ne hant ge - smo-gen
le - ben. de - hei - nen rât kond ich ge - ge - ben, wie

man driu dinc er - wur - be, der kei - nes niht ver -

dur - be diu zwei sint ê - re und varn - de guot, daz

dicke ein an - der scha - den tuot. daz drit - te ist go - tes
der zwei - er ü - ber-

hul - de.
gul - de.
die wolte ich gerne in ei - nen schrīn: jā

lei - der desn mac niht ge - sīn, daz guot und welt - lich

ê - re und go - tes hul - de mê - re ze -

sa - mene in ein her - ze ko - men: stīge und we - ge sint in be -

no - men.
un - triuwe ist in der sā - ze,
ge - walt vert ūf der strā - ze,

fride und reht sint se - re wunt
diu

driu en - ha - bent ge - lei - tes niht, diu zwei en - wer - den

ê   ge - sunt.   (Instrumental)

Walter. Lange Ton

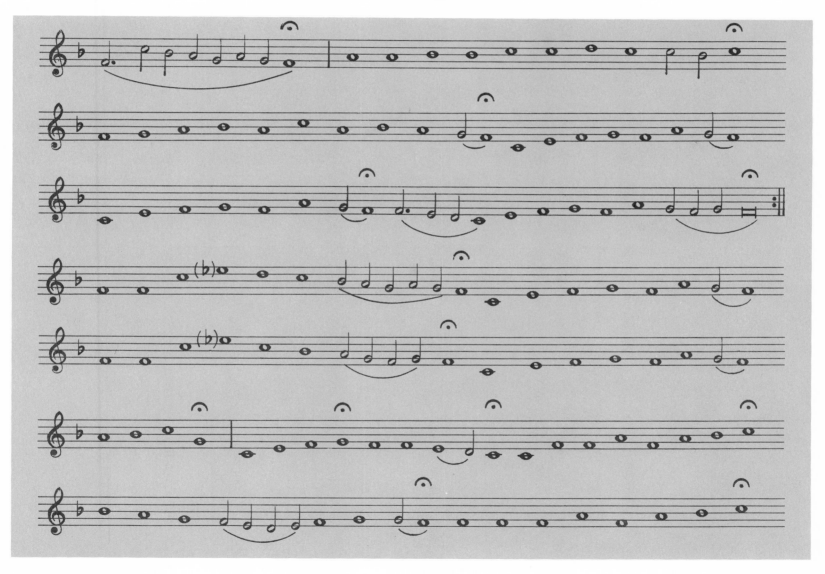

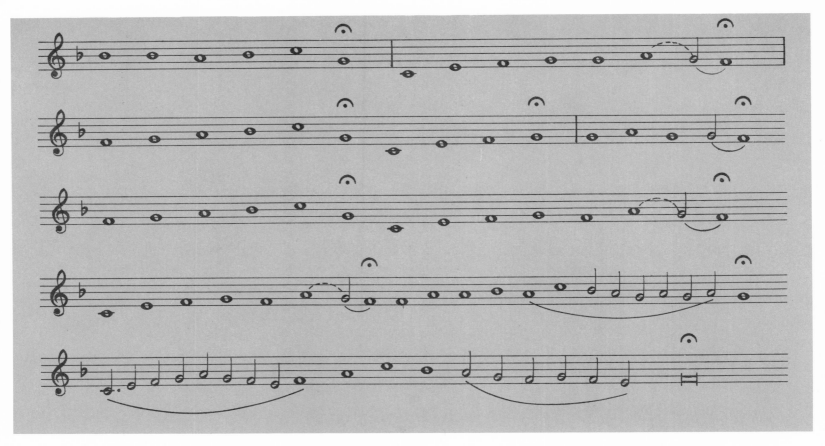

Source of Melody, Wroclaw, Biblioteka Universytecka, Ms. 356 (Adam Puschman's *Singebuch*). Manuscript reported lost in World War II.
Transcription based on G. Münzer, *Das Singebuch des Adam Puschman nebst den Originalmelodien* (Leipzig, Breitkopf & Härtel, 1906), p. 56.

and wretched kings reveal their greed.
Lord Philip, wear the diadem
and bid us follow where you lead!

The "Lange Ton" ascribed to Walther in Adam Pusch-man's songbook illustrates the problem faced by scholars trying to adapt meistersinger songs to minnesinger texts. Many lines of the text require repeats not in the tune to produce the proper number of lines of similar metric structure; some repeats in the music do not correspond to the line lengths of the text; some lines which apparently were at one time repeated are broken up in the meister-singer tune to fit short text lines and must be patched back together for the longer lines of Walther's poem; some of the *Blumen* must be set in syllabic style while others must be treated as ornaments. Thus, the resulting setting is less a transcription than a rather free adaptation of the tune. In the version given here, the opening ornament is treated as a textless introduction, like those in the Montfort songs (see p. 202). The closing ornament must be broken up into syllables to fit the text, but in this arrangement has been repeated as a textless postlude. The complete tune as recorded by Adam Puschman is given for purposes of comparison. Since the manuscript was apparently destroyed during World War II the tune is given in the transcription into modern notation made by Münzer.

Sir Gerhart Atze Shot My Horse
(*Mir hat her Gerhart Atze ein pfert*)

Since there are records of a Gerhart Atze at the Thuringian court and since Walther in another poem refers to him and to the loss of his horse, it is probable that the incident related here actually occurred. Even though the song is bitter, it is not without humor, as when Walther asks someone to hold his staff so that he can make an oath with both hands raised. The "mutual lord" was, of course, Count Hermann.

Sir Gerhart Atze shot my horse
at Eisenache dead.
My grievances I now shall lay
before our mutual lord.
The beast was worth a lot, of course,
but just hear what he said
when it appeared he'd have to pay
the debt that he'd ignored.
He speaks of pain and need
and says my horse indeed
was brother to the steed
which bit his thumb in half
and caused him grief thereby.
I swear with both hands high
all that is just a lie.
Who here will hold my staff?

With Joy May I Arise Today
(*Mit saelden müeze ich hiute ufsten*)

The *Ton* of this *Spruch* was probably composed in honor of Duke Friedrich of Austria, who died in Palestine in 1198. Walther used it more frequently than any other, for a total of fifteen different poems.

With joy may I arise today,
Lord God, and in thy keeping stay,
although I ride from one land to another.
Lord Christ, let there be seen in me
the power of Thy charity,
and keep me for the sake of Thy dear mother.

An angel guarded her from danger
and Thee, when Thou wert in the manger,
as man so young, as God so old.
With humble service and with firm endeavor
among the beasts did Gabriel
watch Mary and her Infant well
and loyally within the fold.
So care for me, and let Thy mercy never
Thy blessed grace from me withhold.

Two melodies from the Colmar manuscript and three from Adam Puschman's songbook are ascribed to Walther and believed to be either meistersinger contrafacts of Walther's melodies or imitations of what the meistersingers thought were Walther's structures. By exercising a certain amount of ingenuity, it is possible to make these melodies fit some of Walther's poems. "Mit saelden müeze ich hiute ufsten" will fit the "Hoffwyse oder Wendelwyse" of the Colmar manuscript. Several slurs of the original have been omitted in this reconstruction.

The Cooks Who Serve Our Host
(*Wir suln den kochen raten*)

Walther, who was perhaps the keenest political analyst of his day, saw great danger to German unity in the increasing strength and number of the semi-autonomous states which were springing up as a result of imperial grants. In this satiric poem he tells the cooks (the advisers and officials of the emperor) to cut off even thicker slices of the Empire for the princes. He then reminds them of the fate of the Byzantine emperor whose country was divided up by the leaders of the crusaders and who was finally deposed.

The cooks who serve our host
and carefully dispense his store
their fears should overcome
and cut the princes' roast
a little larger than before
and thicker by a thumb.
A tasty roast was carved in Greece
with vulgar manners and caprice,

Mir hat her Gerhart Atze ein pfert

Mir hat her Ger-hart At-ze ein pfert er - schoz-zen z̄ I-se-
Ez was wol dri-er mar-ke wert, nu hoe-rent fröm-de

na - che; daz klage ich dem, den er be-stat: derst un - ser
sa - che; sit daz ez an ein gel-ten gat, wa mit er

bei - der vo - get. Er seit von gro-zer swae - re, wie daz min
mich nu zo - get. dem ros-se sip-pe wae - re, daz im den

pfe - rit mae - re.
vin - ger a - be ge - biz-zen hat ze schan-

den: ich swer mit bei-den han - den, daz si sich

niht er - kan - den, ist ie - man der mir sta - be?

Source of Melody, Wroclaw, Biblioteka Universytecka, Ms. 356 (Adam Puschman's *Singebuch*). Manuscript reported lost in World War II.
Transcription based on Münzer, *Das Singebuch des Adam Puschman*, p. 57.

Mit saelden müeze ich hiute ufsten

Mit sael-den müe-ze ich hiute uf-sten, got her-re in di-ner huo-te gen und
Krist her-re, laz mir wer-den schin die gro-zen kraft der güe-te din, und

ri - ten swar ich in dem lan-de ke - re.
pflic min wol dur di - ner muo-ter e - re. Als ir der hei-lig

en - gel pflae-ge, unt din, der in der krip-pen lae - ge, —

jun-ger mensch und al-ter got, De - müe-tic vor dem e-sel und vor dem

rin - de, und doch mit sael-den - ri-cher huo-te —— pflac din Ga-bri-

el der guo-te — wol mit triu-wen sun-der spot: als pflig ouch min, daz

an mir iht er - win - de — din vil gö-te-lich ge-bot.

Source of melody, "Her Walthers von der Vogelweyde hoffwyse oder wendelwys," Munich, Staatsbibliothek, Cod. germ. 4997, f. 734 (the Colmar manuscript).

*The manuscript has two more *g*'s which must be omitted in reconstructing the melody to fit Walther's text.

**The grouping in the manuscript is ♩ ♩ ♩ ♩ .

Wir suln den kochen raten

Wir suln den ko - chen ra -
Daz si der für - sten bra -

ten, sit ez in al - so ho - he
ten, — sni - den groe - zer baz dan

ste, daz si sich niht ver - su - men;
e doch di -cker ei - nes du - men.

Ze Kriechen wart ein spiz versniten,
daz tet ein hant mit argen siten
(sin möht ez niemer han vermiten):
der brate was ze dünne.
Des muose der herre für die tür,
die fürsten sazen ander kür:
der nu daz riche also verlür,
dem stüende baz daz er nie spiz gewünne.

"Der zweite Philippston," Münster, Staatsarchiv, Ms. VII, 51. Fragment, f. 2.
Text in manuscript with music, "Mir hat ein lieht von Franken."

they should have left it in one piece,
the roast was sliced too thin.
The princes forced their host to go
and chose another one for show.
Who loses his possessions so
were better off were he no roast to win.

Four of Walther's poems use the *Ton* which fits this
melody from the Münster fragment. Only the first *Stollen*
is present in the manuscript. Huisman pointed out the
resemblance between this tune and a Christmas song,
"Nu sis uns willekomen hero Christ,"[6] and Gennrich made
a reconstruction of the whole song partly on this basis.[7]
Only the fragment actually in the manuscript is given
here. The transcription is in modal rhythm.

[6]Huisman, *Neue Wege zur . . . Technik,* p. 137.
[7]Gennrich, *Troubadours, Trouvères, Minnesang and Meistergesang,* pp. 52, 72.

Vil wol gelopter got

Vil wol ge-lop-ter got, wie sel-ten ich dich prise! sit
ich von dir bei-de wort han un-de wi-se, wie ge-
tar ich so ge-fre-veln un-der di-me ri-se?

Ichn tuon diu rehten werc, ichn han die waren minne
ze mim ebenkristen, herre vater, noch ze dir;
so holt enwart ich ir dekeinem nie so mir:
Krist, vater unde sun, din geist berihte mine sinne.

Wie solt ich den ge-min-nen der mir ü-be-le tuot? Mir
muoz der ie-mer lie-ber sin der mir ist guot: ver-
gib mir an-ders mi-ne schul-de, ich wil noch ha-ben den muot.

Münster, Staatsarchiv, Ms. VII, 51. Fragment, f. 2.

Thou Most Exalted God,
How Rare My Praise to Thee
(Vil wol gelobter got, wie selten ich dich prîse)

There is no sham or self-deception in Walther's religious expressions. Here he sorrowfully but honestly acknowledges his inability to practice doctrinal Christian love.

Thou most exalted God, how rare my praise to Thee,
although Thou giveth both my song and melody!
How could I so neglect to honor Thy decree?
My works are not the best, nor do I show true love
to Thee, my gracious Lord, nor to my Christian
   brother.
I always cared more for myself than for another.
Oh Father, Son, Thy spirit guide me from above!
How may I love the one who causes me to smart?
I must prefer the man who always takes my part.
Forgive my other sins, I cannot change my heart.

This fragment is one of the surviving parts of the Münster fragment. The only section remaining of the tune is found with the last tercet of the stanza, which ends on the top of a page. In the Colmar manuscript, where unfortunately the melody is completely missing, the *Ton* of the poem is said to have a "split melody" (*gespalten wys*). On the basis of this description, Birkner and others have concluded that the same melody fits the first tercet of the stanza, making the form of the whole A B A, with the B section lost.[8] Certain adjustments must be made in the first part to make it fit, but since the same kinds of changes occur in repeated sections of other minnesongs as a matter of course, it is likely that they are not inappropriate here.

[8]Ursula Aarburg, "Melodien zum frühen deutschen Minnesang," *Zeitschrift für deutsches Altertum,* LXXXVI (1955–56), 24. See also the transcription by Birkner in Friedrich Maurer, *Die Lieder Walthers von der Vogelweide,* I (Tübingen, Max Niemeyer, 1962), 53.

The Early Realists

Neidhart
von Reuenthal

Aₛ ᴡᴀs ᴛʜᴇ ᴄᴀsᴇ with Walther von der Vogelweide, we know no more of Neidhart than can be derived from occasional personal references in his poems. These tell of a knight who owned a modest estate and sang at the court of Duke Ludwig I of Bavaria. He took part in a crusade, perhaps that of 1217–19, and some fourteen years after his return fell out of favor with the new ruler, Duke Otto II. As a result, he lost his property and was obliged to leave Bavaria to find a new protector. He went to Austria and was granted a small fief by Duke Friedrich II, who was himself a minnesinger. Later he apparently entered the service of the Austrian nobleman Otto von Lengenbach. Neidhart must have been born about 1190, and he died sometime after the year 1236.

In the verse of Neidhart one sees the decline of the courtly minnesong with its knights and ladies and chivalric concepts, and the emergence of an entirely new type—the courtly village song. This verse employed the sophisticated and aristocratic form of the minnesong to treat peasant life and scenes. There is no chivalry here, no *Frauendienst,* and no attempt to idealize. In lilting dance melodies Neidhart sings of rustic people and events with the superior, often mocking tones of the nobleman, and spices his colorful reality with burlesque humor. All but one of his songs fall into two groups, the summer songs and the winter songs. The former were probably written in the early part of Neidhart's career and, in keeping with the season and the poet's youth, are generally more light-hearted and spirited than the latter. Most of the winter songs were composed while Neidhart was living in Austria. The structures of the two types of songs also differ, in that the summer songs have a bipartite stanza, whereas the winter songs have the traditional tripartite stanza, made up of two *Stollen* and an *Abgesang.* Both summer and winter songs usually begin with a stanza which describes the season and is followed by stanzas which dramatically relate some village incident. This narrative frequently does not carry over into the last stanza, which deals rather with the poet's own hopes, joys, or sorrows, and often contains his name. Although the narrator takes part in the village activities and even competes with the rude farmers for the favors of the rustic maidens, it should not be

Ine gesach die heide

Ine ge - sach die hei - de nie
baz ge - stalt, in lieh - ter ou - gen-
wei - de den grüe - nen walt:
bî den bei - den kie - se wir den
mei - en, ir mägde, ir sult iuch
zwei - en, gein dir - re lieh-ten
su - mer - zît in hô - hem
muo - te rei - en.

assumed that these accounts are autobiographical. Neidhart played and sang for dances, it is true, but these were held in the halls or gardens of castles, and the dancers were knights and ladies.

Neidhart's songs were very popular in his day and were frequently imitated by minnesingers throughout the entire subsequent history of the minnesong. Nearly six hundred of Neidhart's stanzas are extant, and more melodies have survived for Neidhart's songs than for those of any other minnesinger of his century. Five manuscripts contain songs attributed to him. Those containing most of the texts believed to be genuine Neidhart songs date from the fourteenth and fifteenth centuries, the earliest one from about a century after his death. Although Neidhart was familiar with the minnesongs of his predecessors, he was influenced less by them than by the ruder art of the wandering entertainers, *Vaganten* and *Spielleute,* who sang for the peasants and the townspeople.

Such Delightful Meadows
(*Ine gesach die heide*)

Neidhart would have sung this song at a dance in the courtyard or garden of a castle. It may have been that he sang the first stanza while the dance leaders were going through the first step of the dance, paused while the step was performed by the entire group, sang the second stanza while the leaders performed the second step, etc.

Such delightful meadows
I've never seen,
such changing shades and shadows
of forest green.
May reveals itself in wood and heather.
Come, maidens, all together
and dance a merry roundelay to greet the summer
weather.

Praise from many voices
now hails the May,
and field and wood rejoices
in colors gay,
where before were seen no leaves or flowers.

Beneath the linden bowers
a group of youths and pretty maidens dance away
the hours.
No one's heart is laden
with grief or care.
Come, each shapely maiden,
so sweet and fair,
deck thyself as Swabians desire thee,
Bavarians admire thee,
with silken ribbons on thy blouse from neck to hips
attire thee.

"Why bother?" answered, weeping,
a village maid.
"The stupid men are sleeping,
so I'm afraid.
Honor and delight are but a fable,
the men are all unstable,
to court a woman faithfully and well, they're quite
unable."

"Let's hear no more of sadness,"
thus spoke her friend,
"We'll all grow old with gladness,
for there's no end
of suitors for a maid who's good, and jolly.
Such mournful talk is folly;
I have a lover that can drive away all melancholy."

"If thou canst show a lover
for whom I'd care,
this belt thy waist shall cover
which now I wear.
Tell his name whom thou art thus commending,
whose love is so unending.
I dreamed of thee last night and learned that thou
art just pretending."

"Everybody knows him
as Reuenthal.
His merry songs disclose him
to one and all.
I like him and repay him for his singing.
For him shall I be springing
about in all my finery. But hark, the bell is ringing."

Blôzen wir den anger ligen sâhen

Like most of Neidhart's summer songs, "Ine gesach die heide" has a through-composed melody. It begins in the major mode, although the middle phrases suggest the Dorian mode. The melodic line is noteworthy for the number of thirds and broken triads which it contains; these combine with the major mode to give it a very modern ring.

Barren Were the Meadows and Forsaken
(*Blôzen wir den anger ligen sâhen*)

The poem begins with a nature introduction, continues with a conversation between two village maidens, and ends with an argument between one of the girls and her mother. Neidhart builds several of his songs around such arguments. In them one can see clearly the influence of the *Vaganten,* who were particularly fond of the Middle Latin *altercatio,* or argumentative song.

Barren were the meadows and forsaken
until the summer came to warm and waken,
flowers pressed through grass and clover then.
Once again
summer now is opening the roses
and making lovely heath and glen.

Nightingale and thrush, we hear them singing,
with the sound the hills and vales are ringing.
They sing their songs of joyous summertime
as they climb.
May has brought us happiness and beauty:
the heath is blooming in its prime.

Spoke a maid, "The dew is on the heather,
see the splendor summer brings together.
The trees that in the wintertime were bare
everywhere
wave their leafy branches in the breezes.
The nightingales are singing there.

"Losa, hear the songs of birds resounding,
they greet the May from all the trees surrounding.
I fancy, we are free of winter now.
Wierat, thou

must dance more spritely, would'st thou gain my
    favor,
beneath the linden's leafy bough.

"Spring's the time for each to choose a lover.
Roses blossom 'neath the forest's cover
and I shall have a crown of roses red
on my head
when I'm dancing hand in hand so gaily
with such a handsome knight," she said.

"Daughter, think no more of bold advances.
Should'st thou disturb the nobles at the dances,
who are not the sort for folk as we,
I foresee
thou willst have a lot of pain and trouble.
A sturdy farmer covets thee."

"Let a heifer wed the worthy farmer!
My hope is for a stately knight in armor.
Why should I take a farmer as my man?
Never can
I be happy with a rustic lover.
A knight alone will suit my plan."

"Daughter, don't despise his lowly station
to win a stupid noble's admiration.
This has caused your friends distress and pain.
All in vain
are thy promises, I tell thee truly,
thy willfulness I never could restrain."

"Mother mine, stop scolding, and believe me,
I would love him though my friends should leave
    me,
I never hid my wishes, I recall.
One and all
may the people know whom I have chosen,
for he's the knight of Reuenthal."

Below is an alternate version of the text. The first line of this version begins with an unaccented syllable for which the up-beat *d* should be used.

So schoenen wir den anger nie gesahen,
do uns diu sumerzit begunde nahen;

Kint, bereitet iuch der sliten ûf daz îs!

Kint, be — rei — tet iuch der sli — ten
man — ger grüe — nen lin — den stênt ir

ûf daz îs! da ist der lei — de
tol — den grîs; un — be — sun — gen

win — der kalt: der hât uns der
ist der walt: daz ist al — lez

wün — nec — lî — chen bluo — men vil be —
von des rî — fen un — ge — nâ — den

no — men.
ko — men. Mugt ir schou — wen,

wie er hât die hei — de er — zo —

gen? Die ist von sî — nen schul — den

val.   dar   zuo   sint   die   nah – ti –

gal   al – le ir   wec   ge – vlo – gen.

Berlin Ms. germ. 779, f. 236.

die bou den winter stuonden val:
über al
sint si niuwes loubes riche worden,
darunder singt vrou nahtegal.

The musical notation of this song is of special interest since it is the only song in the Berlin Neidhart manuscript which is recorded in rhythmic notation and is therefore the earliest minnesong which appears in mensural notation. It was added to the manuscript by a second scribe, probably somewhat later than the other songs. The length of the rests is not notated; rather haphazard lines show the ends of the phrases. Since the rhythm shown in this manuscript is the typical long-short pattern of modal rhythm (except for the three long notes of the three-syllable line), the existence of this notation is an argument in favor of modal rhythms in other minnesongs. Of course, the very fact that the song is specifically written in mensural notation might indicate that it was an exception rather than the rule; however, the songs of Neidhart all seem to fit best in the lively rhythms of the iambic mode, and they have been so transcribed in this anthology.

Children, Ice Is Here, So Ready Up a Sleigh
(Kint, bereitet iuch der sliten ûf daz îs!)

Winter songs, such as this, were also sung at dances, but these dances took place, of course, indoors. The first four stanzas contain the nature introduction and the preparation for the dance. The following two stanzas describe an amusing incident at the dance, and the last stanza, which is essentially a *Spruch,* contains the poet's lament at the trials of a property owner.

Children, ice is here, so ready up a sleigh
for the dreary winter's cold.
It has stolen from the meadow all its golden treasure,
crowns of lindens, once so green, have turned to
    gray,
birds have left their forest fold.
All of that has come because we roused the Frost's
    displeasure.
Only see how he through field and heath did wander!
Now their blooms are drab and pale,
now has flown the nightingale
to distant meadows yonder.

I could use the counsel of a prudent friend
on a matter that is pressing:
where shall all the young folks come for merriment
    and playing?
Megenwart has quite a spacious room to lend.
If to this you give your blessing,
there we'll gather on the holiday for roundelaying,
for his daughter wants us and it isn't far.
Tell your friends, they must, if able,

see the dance beneath the table
performed by Engelmar.

Get the news to Kunigund, for she will go,
she loves dancing through and through
and has bitterly complained that she is never told.
Gisel, go to Jiutendorf and let them know,
say that Ella must come too.
They have always been my friends, the young ones
    and the old.
Child, do not forget to speak with Hedwig now
and insist that she be there.
Tell them all, they should not wear
their shawls down to the brow.

As for shawls upon the head, I'll speak my mind
to the women everywhere
who would show their modesty to lovers they
    possess.
Move them higher up in front and down behind,
so your necks will not be bare.
Shawls do little good when there's no collar on the
    dress.
Women always have been safe about the head,
It's secure in any case.
What befalls another place
they also need not dread.

Eppe tried to teach some manners all around
(he was aided by his flail),
but the stick of Master Adelbert brought peace once
    more.
This was started by an egg that Ruprecht found
(or the devil had for sale.)
He would throw it 'cross the room at Eppe, so he
    swore.
Eppe soon was mad as he was bald and thin;
"Don't you dare," he grimly said.
Ruprecht hit him on the head
and egg ran down his chin.

Friedelieb with Gotelinde then was seen:
Engelmar with rage was wild.
If it will not bore you, I'll relate the whole affair.

Eberhard, the farmer, had to step between,
they were partly reconciled,
otherwise they'd each have seized the other by the
    hair.
They, like stupid ganders that had lost their wits,
eyed each other all day long.
He who led the rest in song
was, as always, Fritz.

Once my hair was dressed as fits a cavalier,
brushed and curled in perfect trim.
That is all forgotten in the worries of my fief,
salt and grain I need to buy throughout the year.
How have I offended him
who has burdened stupid me with house and land
    and grief?
Little were the debts to him, which now I rue,
but my curses aren't so small
when I there at Reuenthal
wonder what to do.

Sing, My Golden Cock, I'll Give Thee Grain
(Sinc an, guldîn huon! ich gibe dir weize)

Neidhart begins this song not with his usual salute to
the season but with the plaint, which in other poems appears at the end. It is, of course, possible that this arrangement may have originated with the medieval collectors
of his verse. The references to dances in the poem are
interesting. The *ridewanz* was apparently danced in
groups of three, each one composed of a man and two
women or a woman and two men. It was a lively dance as
compared to the more stately "courtly dance" which the
villagers performed while they caught their breath.

The "fiddle" mentioned in the poem is the medieval
German *gîge,* which was also known as a rebec. It was a
flat-topped, bowed-stringed instrument with a pear-
shaped body like the later lute. It was used for accompany-
ing both singing and dancing, and it is often referred to as
a "merry instrument."

"Sing, my golden cock, I'll give thee grain!"
(at her voice

I rejoice)
spoke the pretty maid for whom I sigh.
Thus a dunce's hopes are raised in vain
seasons through.
Were it true,
no one's spirit then would be so high,
no one else's heart would beat so light.
Will her careless gaiety
ever free
me from all the sorrows of my plight?

Listen! Hear the dancing at the inn!
Every man
go who can,
there the women wait, a merry throng.
Soon we'll see the *ridewanz* begin.
Tarradiddle
goes the fiddle,
lusty peasant youths break forth in song.
Each in turn sings out his verse with pride,
shakes the room with lungs of brass.
Noblegrass
dances with a maid on either side.

Move out all the chairs and clear the floor;
take the tables
to the stables
and we'll dance till feet and ankles hurt.
Open up the windows and the door;
let the breeze
cool their knees,
blowing through each village wench's skirt.
When the leaders stop to rest a little,
then we'll all, great and small,
short and tall,
step a courtly dance once to the fiddle.

Gozbreht, Willebolt, Gumpreht, and Eppe,
Willebrand,
hired hand,
Werenbolt and also youngster Tutze,
Megenbolt, the farmer's son, and Reppe,
Irenwart,
Sigehart,

Giselher and Frideger and Utze—
he's the stupid oaf from Holingare.
He goes courting every day,
so they say,
but the girls don't like him anywhere.

Never has a bumpkin looked so grand,
nor so flighty;
God Almighty,
how he struts in line before the rest!
More than two hands wide the leather band
of his sword,
like a lord
in his new and gaily colored vest,
scraps of every shape and hue are there,
fancy shirt, embroidered pants,
see him prance
in a garb no other fool would wear.

His attire is rustic as can be,
it's absurd.
So I've heard,
he's been wooing Engel's daughter, Pearl.
All such hopes are futile, I foresee.
She's a prize
of shape and size
to win the admiration of an earl.
Good advice I'll give him: let him try
someone else; for all his pain
what he'll gain
he can take to Mayence in his eye.

Though his clothes are colorful and gay
and he's dressed
in his best,
he should know, she simply can't abide him.
He has hung around her every day;
I became
red with shame
when I saw her sitting down beside him.
If I win this maid who looks so pretty,
I shall give to her my all,
Reuenthal,
for her own: this is my fabled city.

Sinc an, guldîn huon! ich gibe dir weize
(version A)

Sinc an, guldîn huon! ich gibe dir weize
(version B)

"Sinc an, guldîn huon" is found in both the Berlin and Frankfurt Neidhart manuscripts and is one of the few minnesinger examples of variant versions of the same song. The earlier manuscript (Frankfurt) has a somewhat more highly embellished melody than does the Berlin collection. This might mean that the later scribe was familiar with a simplified version of the melody, that the Frankfurt collector included ornaments added by the singer from whom he heard the tune, or even that he might have added them to display his own skill. Both tunes are in *Barform* with a return of the last part of the *Stollen* melody. In the Berlin manuscript, this return is slightly ornamented.

Winter's Evil Art
(*Winter, dîniu meil*)

The incongruities which characterize so much of Neidhart's work are nowhere more obvious than in this song. It begins with the apparent sincerity of a true love song, but, as it continues, we see a grotesquely amusing hero develop, a knight who is in love with a peasant girl whom he addresses as "lady mine." He is a most unknightly knight who is bullied and frightened by his country bumpkin rivals. The final stanza, however, reverts to the sincere and lyric mood of the beginning. The next-to-the-last stanza is interesting in that it seems to be a parody of a stanza in Walther's song, "Ir sult sprechen: 'willekomen.'" One stanza of the original was omitted in the translation.

> Winter's evil art
> strips the forest of its leaves
> and flowers from the blooming earth.
> Summer, joy has vanished from thy merry retinue.
> Many a happy heart
> now in bitter sadness grieves
> which was made for only mirth.
> How could a maid whom I before all others would
>   pursue
> still appear
> not to hear
> the serenade with pleasure

> which I sang with all the fervor I possess
> and yet today preserve and treasure
> that she may never find a limit to my faithfulness.

> Should my constancy
> and devotion through the year
> afford me naught but her rejection,
> then might I repent, and rightly, this unhappy
>   quest.
> It was told to me,
> who was always faithful here
> would gain in fortune and affection.
> With thee to comfort, Lady Luck, my hope is for the
>   best:
> that she may mend
> and show her friend
> less extreme vexation.
> Could this be, perhaps the end might still be good.
> Grant her evil temper moderation!
> Woe, that women never treat their lovers as they
>   should.

> For this love of mine
> many wish me only ill.
> Now hear my plaint with sympathy,
> never have I needed wise and prudent counsel
>   more.
> Erph and Adelwine
> cause me trouble still,
> before my time this ages me.
> No one can imagine what I've suffered heretofore.
> All this year,
> so I hear,
> they have sought her favor
> whom I'll always love and wish to be my own.
> Mistress of a heart that ne'er shall waiver,
> thou shallst never comfort any man but me alone.

> Thou must lock the door
> which will close those ears of thine,
> that they no jealous words may hear
> which might make me seem to thee otherwise than
>   good.
> Mark such talk no more,

Winter, dîniu meil

Berlin Ms. germ. 779, f. 231.

*An apparent error in the manuscript places the last thirteen notes a third higher and contains one too few notes for the syllables in the line.

Oh my darling, lady mine,
that is not fitting for thy ear.
Listen to a faithful friend's advice, as each one
    should.
Kuenebrecht,
Engeknecht,
forward and deceiving,
sue for thy affection. Lady, have them go.
They are why my loving heart is grieving,
they have ever been the source of secret bitter woe.

Only see my hair,
it is colored like the snow!
Despite my age it makes me gray
that I suffer grief from peasant louts because of her.
There is Engelmare;
he's a reason I am so.
The mirror he still has today
which he once did take from Vriderun, the villager.
From then on

I have gone
courting her no longer,
save with timid steps and timid heart and fear,
and my sorrow waxes ever stronger
that my aching heart desires the maid whom he
    holds dear.

Westward to the Rhine,
from the Elbe to the Po,
I know the countries all around.
All their borders do not hold so many brazen louts
as a county line
here in Austria, you know.
Many new ones every day are found.
See, there's one who's caused a lot of trouble
    hereabouts:
Wankelbolt,
he's a dolt,
me he would discredit
(he's a leader there in Lyingdale, it's said),

and the bastard really will regret it.
If he gets too saucy, I'll put holes right through his
  head.

Love once came to me:
Oh, if love had but remained!
I came and found the roses fair.
See, I plucked a rose, but soon it lost its loveliness.
Pain and misery
drove away the joy I gained.
I'll tell what I discovered there:
I broke the rose, a wretched thorn then caused me
  sore distress,

so that I,
though I sigh,
let no roses prick me,
neither look to see what roses I may find.
Many roses raise their thorns to stick me,
but I know there still are roses which are kind.

It would be possible to transcribe the three-syllable lines as spondees, as in the short line of the mensurally notated "Blôzen wir den anger ligen sâhen." The transcription would then read as follows for the beginning of the *Abgesang:*

Reinmar von Zweter

OF THE MANY disciples and imitators of Walther von der Vogelweide among the younger generation of the early thirteenth century, the most prolific was Reinmar von Zweter. There are no historical records of this minnesinger, and all that we know of him is that which can be gleaned from his songs. He was born in the middle Rhine area about the year 1200, but grew up in Austria, perhaps at the court of Leopold VI and Friedrich II. It is quite likely that he became acquainted with Walther at this time. From Austria Reinmar went to Bohemia, where he spent at least four years at the court of King Wenzel I. A wandering life followed, which was interrupted by fairly lengthy stays at Meissen and Mainz. He died about the year 1260. According to the tradition of the meistersingers, he was blind.

One religious *Leich* and 229 one-stanza songs by Reinmar are extant. All of the latter are composed in the same *Ton* and, with few exceptions, are *Sprüche* rather than minnesongs. Like Walther, Reinmar was very much interested in the social and political situation of his times. He, too, opposed the domination of the papacy and advocated a strong empire. He was also concerned with religious and spiritual matters, to which many of his songs are devoted. Almost all of Reinmar's compositions, even those dealing with love, are strongly didactic. Often, following the tradition of Spervogel, he clothes his moral teachings in the form of animal fables.

Reinmar viewed the world about him as a clear-eyed realist and described it in a direct, rather blunt, and sometimes humorous manner. He possessed little lyrical talent and, judging from the fact that his songs all employ the same *Ton*, probably even less musical talent. However, despite these obvious limitations, he is second only to Walther as a composer of *Sprüche*. With regard to the history of the German lyric, Reinmar is important for having introduced the minnesong and the *Spruch* into Bohemia and for the influence which he exerted on later Bohemian singers.

Es wont ein magt uff erden hie

Donaueschingen, Fürstlich-Fürstenbergische Bibliothek, Hs. 120, f. 233.

Upon This Earth Once Lived a Maid
(*Es wont ein magt uff erden hie*)

Reinmar was one of the favorite poets of the meister-singers and was widely imitated by them. Such a song as this may have inspired the many compositions which they produced in praise of the Virgin Mary.

Upon this earth once lived a maid;
she sent her messengers   and for the Son of God
    they prayed,
her innocence, her modesty,   her humbleness, her
    purity
with all their power God did ask
that He would give to her   the pure and most
    exalted task
that she, a maid, might bear Him,   as an angel
    promised it should be.
And when her messengers the news had heard,
and when they brought to her the joyous word,
the Holy Spirit showed in her His might.
She saw the Child, this maiden blessed,
just as It lay beneath her breast
till It was born. How can we pay her right?

The transcription is in modal rhythm, with the occasional dactyls of the text transcribed as even quarter notes. The little melisma at the end may be a meister-singer's addition, since the Donaueschingen manuscript is fairly late.

Sir Cock, I Grant to You the Prize
(*Her Han, ich wil iu siges jehen*)

It is indicative of the changing times and of the decline of the cult of *minne* that a knight should treat women so harshly as Reinmar does in this humorous song. The *Ton* and melody are that of the preceding song.

Sir Cock, I grant to you the prize,
you're really very brave   as I have seen with my
    own eyes.
You're master in your house   though you've more
    wives than most think necessary.

As for myself, I've only one.
She's soured all my thoughts   and spoiled all my
    fun,
she wears the pants, you know,   and loudly
    scolds whenever I am merry.
If I had two of her, I'd laugh no more,
my joys would disappear, if I had four,
I'd pine away, if I had eight,
they'd surely be the death of me.
Sir Cock, keep well the bravery
that rules a dozen hens and frees their mate.

"Salve Regina, Mater Misericordiae"
("*Salve regina, mater misercordie*")

In addition to the songs which are definitely by Reinmar von Zweter, there are twenty-four songs of somewhat dubious authorship which have been attributed to him by medieval anthologists. This song belongs to the latter group. The *Ton,* though much more embellished, is not unlike that customarily employed by Reinmar.

"Salve regina, mater misericordiae!
This greeting do I bring to thee, thou queen most
    high!
I hail thee, lady of charity, this day!"
Only she may thus be greeted, she alone,
for none like she is on the earth or heaven's throne,
she guides the stranger on his lonely way.
Though you may journey early or late,
she blesses you and never will forsake you.
The power of our queen is great,
rejoice, therefore, and let not fear o'ertake you.
Come soon, I counsel everyone,
for late remorse is less reward to win,
whatever child of man has done
bring her your pain for she can conquer sin.
The judge she carries on her arm
will grant her each request,
and she'll protect you from all harm.
Fear no alarm,
the queen of mercy still can charm
and guide all for the best.

"Salve regina, mater misercordie!"

The Marian antiphon "Salve regina, mater misericordiae" was probably written by Hermannus Contractus, who died in 1054. It was the subject of sermons from 1100 on, and soon became a favorite with hymn writers who wrote sermonizing hymns meditating on each phrase of the antiphon in a separate stanza of the hymn. The tune of Reinmar's paraphrase has a very beautiful effect if sung in the free rhythm of the Solesmes method of Gregorian chant, even though the melodic structure of the cadences suggests that it has a secular origin. In this transcription the cadence melismas are to be performed with each note, rather than each syllable, of equal value.

O God and Thy Eternal Reign
(*God vnd dyn ewen ewykit*)

This song consists of the first two segments of Reinmar's single *Leich*, a rather long work in which he sings of divine love.

O God and Thy eternal reign,
supported by a Trinity,
may Thou be praised, because our pain
was driven forth by one of three,

and this One is a son to Thee.
  Through Thy command this earth He trod,
and for our soul's salvation bled,
He died as man and not as God,
He died in human grief and dread.
His death has gained us life instead.

The longest musical form used by the minnesingers was the *Leich,* derived from the Romance *lai,* which in turn was constructed on the same principles as the Latin sequence. In the German form, the structure is a long series of groups of verses (*Leich* segments) using the same melody with first and second endings for each double verse of the *Leich* segment. Each segment has a different melody, although varied forms of the same or similar materials may reappear freely throughout the *Leich*. The musical form of Reinmar's *Leich* is interesting for the added phrases after most of the double versicles. There are twenty-nine different musical sections, and in sections 1-6, 28, and 29 the same musical refrain is used at the end of the section, although there is no refrain in the text. The segments given here show the first two double versicles with their musical refrain.

God vnd dyn ewen ewykit

God vnd dyn e - wen e - wy - kit mit dryn per - so - nen

vn - der schri - ben, si des ge - lopt, daz vn - ser leyt der dry - er

MUSICAL REFRAIN

ey - ner hat vor tri - ben, der dir czu kyn - de ist be -

li - ben. Der sel - be wart durch dyn ge - bot vnd ouch durch vn - sir

heyl vor sni - ten. Des starb her mensch vnd starp nicht got, her starp al nach menschi-

MUSICAL REFRAIN

li - chen si - ten. Syn ster - ben hat vn - ser leben er - stri - ten.

Vienna, Nationalbibliothek, Hs. 2701, f. 11.

*The manuscript has an extra *e* for this syllable.

Tannhäuser

TANNHÄUSER was born about the year 1200 as a younger (and therefore propertyless) son of Bavarian or Austrian minor nobility. He appears in no historical records, and our knowledge of him is derived solely from personal references in his works. These tell of an adventurous, exuberant, and wastrel life. In the early part of his career Tannhäuser was a protégé of Friedrich II of Austria and his two sons, Heinrich and Konrad. From Friedrich the singer received extensive properties which enabled him to carry on a gay existence at the court, interrupted only by his participation in the crusade of 1228–29 and the Cyprian War two years later. With the death of Friedrich in 1246 Tannhäuser's carefree life was over, and the difficult existence of the penniless minstrel began. For the singer had long since wasted away the property which Friedrich had given him. From then on until his death around 1266, Tannhäuser wandered from court to court, supporting himself meagerly with his songs.

The content of Tannhäuser's *Leiche,* minnesongs, and *Sprüche* is exclusively courtly, but one can readily see that the singer does not take the courtly ethic or the ideal of *Frauendienst* seriously. In a humorous and often ironic manner he parodies the chivalric themes much as Heine did those of the nineteenth-century Romanticists. Two contrasting moods predominate in his songs, the one a jovial affirmation of the life of the senses, the other a sad melancholy that such good times as he had experienced should end. Most of his songs and five of his six *Leiche* are composed to dance rhythms, not those of courtly dances, but of lively, even tumultuous village dances. The dance songs, like those of Neidhart, are divided into summer songs and winter songs. Tannhäuser was by nature a realist, not only in his burlesques of outworn themes, but also in his keen interest in the world about him. The songs of no other minnesinger contain so much factual and detailed information as do those of Tannhäuser.

Although Tannhäuser, the man and composer, is today largely forgotten, the Tannhäuser of legend, thanks to Wagner, is well known. Wagner's opera was based on a ballad, the earliest manuscript of which dates from the middle of the fifteenth century. It tells of Tannhäuser's seduction by Venus, his stay in the Venus Mountain, his repentance and his pilgrimage to the Pope, and his final redemption. The legend itself is a very old one and doubtless predates Tannhäuser, who probably became its hero sometime in the fourteenth century. There is no obvious reason why Tannhäuser should have become connected by tradition with the Venus Mountain myth. It is true that some of his songs reveal a penitent mood, but in them he repents the wasting of his wealth, not the loss of his soul.

My Lady Wishes To Reward
(Min frowe diu wil lonen mir)

In this song Tannhäuser parodies the extravagant promises made by lovers in the earlier minnesong and ridicules the theme of *Frauendienst*.

My lady wishes to reward
my service and my loyalty.
Let's thank her, all with one accord,
for having been so kind to me.
I only need to cause the Rhine
to flow no more through Coblenz land
and she will grant a wish of mine.
She'd also like some grains of sand
from out the sea where sets the sun,
then she'll give heed to my request.
She wants a star, the nearest one
will do, it need not be the best.
My love is strong,
whate'er her song
I will not think she does me wrong,   my own.
To God alone
and no one else is this fair lady known.

If from the moon I steal the glow,
then may I have this noble wench.
And she'll reward me well, I know,
if 'round the world I dig a trench.
If like an eagle I might fly,
then would she welcome my advances
(that is, if none could soar so high),
or if I broke a thousand lances

within a day, as did the sire
of Parzival to win the prize,
she'd gladly do what I desire,
'twill cost me plenty otherwise.
My love is strong,
whate'er her song
I will not think she does me wrong,   my own.
To God alone
and no one else is this fair lady known.

If I the Elbe's waters bound,
I'd be rewarded; could I make
the Danube flow without a sound,
she'd love me well, for custom's sake.
A salamander I must bring
to her from searing fire and flame,
then will she grant me anything
that any loving knight might claim.
When I can turn aside the rain
and snow, I've often heard her say,
and make the summer wax and wane,
then I shall have a lover's pay.
My love is strong,
whate'er her song
I will not think she does me wrong,   my own.
To God alone
and no one else is this fair lady known.

It is particularly unfortunate that the music to this song with a refrain is lost, since the refrain has such an interesting metrical structure, contrasting strongly with the even tetrameter lines which precede it.

How Delightful Is This Lovely Day
(Ez ist hiute eyn wunnychlicher tac)

It has been suggested that this song from the Jena manuscript was the cause of Tannhäuser's becoming associated with the Venus Mountain legend. It is also possible, however, that the song was altered in the process of oral transmission to conform with an already established folk tradition such as appears in the Tannhäuser ballad.

Es ist hiute eyn wunnychlicher tac

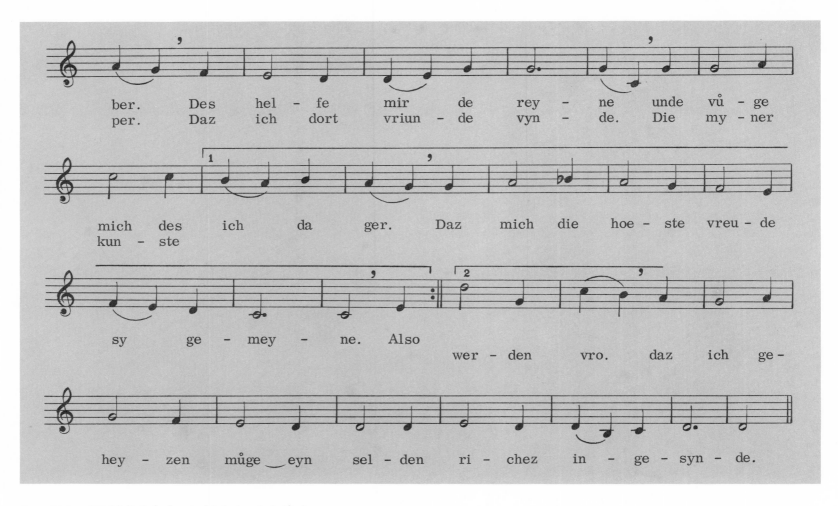

Jena, Universitätsbibliothek, Jenaer Liederhandschrift, f. 42.

*The manuscript has in the first section.

The small notes are to be used for the repeats.

How delightful is this lovely day!
Now care for me Who over all disposes,
that I may ever live with blessing
and may do penance for my worldly blindness.
For He indeed will be my stay
and through His aid my soul secure reposes.
May I be healed of all transgressing
and may I yet obtain God's loving kindness.

Grant me a will which shall not bend
and which deserves His love so well
that God may well reward me!
May I but have a happy end,
and may my soul in rapture dwell,
a gentle death afford me.
May I be saved by purity,
that hell may be no danger.

What I require, give unto me,
that I to highest joy be not a stranger.
Here must I have no family,
that friends I may have yonder
who take such pleasure in my songs
that I shall be renowned among the knights who
   heavenward wander.

The *Abgesang* of this song shows an interesting reuse of motives and phrases from the *Stollen* and from the first part of the *Abgesang* itself, fitted together in a mosaic-like fashion. The form of the whole song is:

ABCD   ABCD   EFG   EFG′   AG″HI   AG″HJ.

Stollen   *Stollen*   *Abgesang*

The third phrase (C) ends with a descending fifth which reappears as the cadence of lines 11, 16, and 20 (G and the two appearances of G″). The whole of line 4 (D) is incorporated into the long closing line (J), making the closing quatrain begin and end like the *Stollen* melody, but using material from the *Abgesang* in the middle. The treatment of the material introduced in line 11 is quite ingenious (G, G′, and G″). Lines 11 and 14 (G and G′) begin alike but end differently. G″ (lines 16 and 20) begins with a new up-beat and adds one ornamental note, but ends with the same cadence as G (line 11).

The repeated sections reflect the poetic form, which uses a new meter and rhyme scheme for the verse triplet with which the *Abgesang* begins. The whole form resembles the structure of a *Leich* (three segments).

The Later Thirteenth Century

Alexander

THE SONGS of Alexander, referred to in some manuscripts as "The Wild Alexander," in others as "Master Alexander," tell us little about the author's life. We know that he was a Swabian, a wandering singer of humble birth, that he composed during the second half of the thirteenth century, and no more. Of his compositions one *Leich* and forty-one stanzas of songs are extant, the latter consisting mainly of *Sprüche.*

Alexander was a man of strong religious feelings who exhorted with the voice of an Old Testament prophet against the evils of a worldly life. The designation "The Wild," however, does not describe his utterance, but only refers to his wandering life. His verse is characterized by a darkness and indefiniteness of expression, an obscure symbolism and allegory. It abounds in biblical allusions. The few minnesongs which he composed lack the note of conviction which permeates his didactic verse and were obviously only created to satisfy the demands of his audience.

Long Ago as Boys Together
(*Hie bevorn do wir kynder waren*)

If this song were what it at first appears, a simple tale of childhood, it would be almost unique in Middle High German lyric verse. Unfortunately, however, as we discover in the final stanza, it is not such a tale, but instead is an allegory in which the listener is warned to renounce the things of the world. The allusion is to the foolish virgins of the New Testament parable. It has been suggested that the song was inspired by Vergil's third eclogue.

Long ago as boys together
we would race in summer weather
free as any careless rover
through the blooming fields of clover,
and in calmer hours
gather flowers
where you see the cows and drover.

I remember, we were bending
down to pick the blooms, contending
which the fairest were, and we

Hie bevorn do wir kynder waren

wove us wreaths and danced with glee,
childish faces beaming,
flowers streaming,
in those times that used to be.

Seeking berries, we would wander
to the distant beeches yonder,
over stick and stone would run
till the setting of the sun,
till the forest ranger
(then no stranger)
said, "Go home now. Day is done."

Though we got a lot of scratches
racing through the berry patches,
that was sport, we did not care.
Shepherds told us to beware,
when they saw us playing,
always saying,
"Children, snakes are everywhere."

Once a playmate, who was lying
in a thicket, rushed out, crying,
"There's a snake! Where it is stony!
It's the one that bit our pony,
so that we can never
cure him ever.
He is still so sick and bony."

Leave the forest and your playing,
go at once, without delaying,
or you'll suffer great distress.
If you linger, nonetheless,
in the forest vale,
you'll bewail
all your vanished happiness.

Once five foolish virgins tarried
when their ruler's son was married,
till at last he locked the hall
and ignored their fearful call
when the watchmen there
stripped them bare,
till they had no clothes at all.

Oh, That One with Love Must Win
(*Owe daz nach liebe gat*)

Alexander was obviously no lover. He has little to say about the joys of love and is rather vague when, as in this poem, he sings of love's sorrows. On the other hand, the simple structure employed here lends itself so well to an immediacy of expression that the total effect is both intimate and pleasing.

Oh, that one with love must win
always much of pain!
Love demands that I begin
verses in this vein.
She herself spoke thus to me:
"Tell of pain beyond all wonder
when two loves are torn asunder
sadly and eternally."

Of me and of my lady too
I well may tell such grief,
for when we pledge that we'll be true
we'll know, without relief,
naught but sorrow every day.
Love has power to enchant us
and for loyalty will grant us
little joy and great dismay.

For when we fell into Love's snare
then all our joys were dead,
but still we lived with heavy care
in sorrow and in dread.
Life is death for every lover;
Lady Love, restrain thy rages,
be more sparing with thy wages!
Let me die and her recover.

Just kill me now and let her live.
Spoke Love, "It shall not be.
To them who wear my crest I give
both joy and misery.
I'd be false to name and art
and from duty would be turning,
should I not distress with yearning
two who are so far apart."

Owe daz nach liebe gat

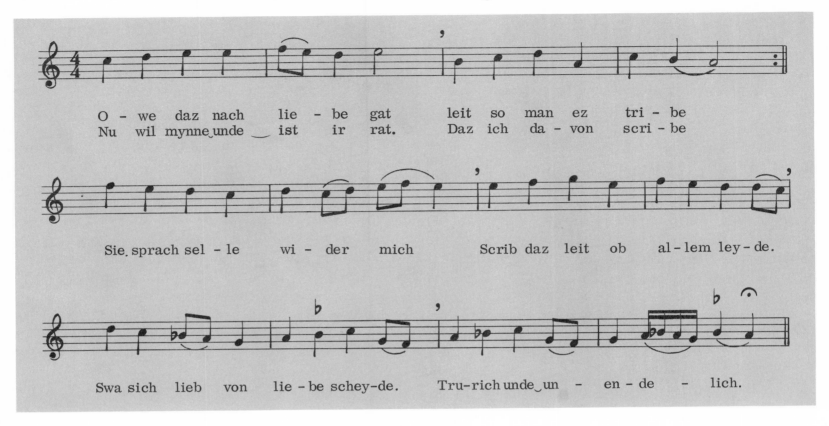

O - we daz nach lie - be gat   leit so man ez tri - be
Nu wil mynne unde ist ir rat.   Daz ich da - von scri - be

Sie sprach sel - le wi - der mich   Scrib daz leit ob al - lem ley - de.

Swa sich lieb von lie - be schey - de.   Tru - rich unde un - en - de - lich.

Jena, Universitätsbibliothek, Jenaer Liederhandschrift, f. 25.

For me a year would be a day,
if she were with me now,
and all my grief would pass away,
if fortune would allow
us such happiness and cheer.
But till then this pain I'll carry
even when my friends are merry,
and each day will be a year.

Like all the earlier minnesongs (except for the one mensurally notated song of Neidhart), the songs in the Jena manuscript are written with no rhythmic indications. In contrast to some of the earlier songs, however, the rhythms of the poetry are often quite conventional and do not lend themselves to the free rhythmic transcriptions used for some songs in the preceding parts of this anthology. Modal rhythms (almost without exception the first mode) or duple meter work equally well for many of the songs. The two preceding examples by Alexander show both meters, one in each song.

"Owe daz nach liebe gat" is found together with his *Leich* in two manuscripts, the Jena manuscript and the Vienna manuscript 509. The two versions are so much alike that it is likely they were both drawn from an earlier manuscript, only slightly altered in the process of transmission. The main difference is the addition of some up-beats in the Vienna manuscript, fitting the extra syllables in the text. For example, the first line of the Jena text begins "Owe daz nach liebe . . ." while the same line in the Vienna version is "Ach, owe daz nach liebe. . . ."

The Cause of My Despairing
(*Myn trurichlichiz klagen*)

Alexander's single long work, this *Minneleich,* well illustrates his general attitude toward the love song. It announces the singer's dedication, not to the service of a particular woman, but to love itself. He anticipates no happiness in the service of love, but accepts it only as a sad duty. The *Leich* consists of twenty-four segments, each having a different metrical structure.

The cause of my despairing
is that I've lost my art
through my woe.
But must I go on, bearing
the sorrow in my heart,
ever so,
the burning torment fanned
by love's command?
   No, I must indeed from such a grief
find quick relief,
the breath
of death
drive away
or be a prey
every day
unceasingly to sorrow's sting.
Just as the swan
who knows anon
the hour when comes his death, as he I sing.
   Oh fruitful vine of all enjoyment,
Oh thou who gives my soul employment,
thou my loyal confidence,
my consolation and defense.
   Ah, love, may I thy gifts esteem,
a stringent life, a precious dream!
Must I leave my lady fair
sword and shield for thee to bear?
   Well may he his fate bemoan
who must bear the shield alone.
That is need beyond all need
when a faithful knight takes up the shield

and leaves with passion unrevealed,
oh, that's a living death indeed.
   So let the twain then come together
they'll be so merry in any weather
that joy above all joy is born.
But sorrow later comes to wreck
their bliss and put them both in check,
parting leaves the pair forlorn.
   Love is the preserver
of him who wants to serve her
faithfully through thick and thin.
Oh, but sorrow is her twin!
   Who her shield would carry
now is sad, now merry.
He must suffer joy and pain
just as love may so ordain.
   We were told
by the old
of desire and dread,
of the many who sped
to the realm of the dead,
struck down by passion's mighty blow.
Inform me,
thou stormy
love, how I may praise
thee and all thy ways
well with pretty lays,
that all thy friends may know.
   And praised be he
who is free
but desires to be the thane
of courtly love for high rewards.
I shall now
tell him how
he may gain, and entertain
with words of love and sweetest chords.
   Now listen, thus the shield is made,
beneath it many bards have played,
a naked child on field of red
with sightless eyes and jeweled head,
a golden arrow in one hand,
the other holds a flaming brand.

Myn trurichlichiz klagen

Ja myn ste-te tzů-vůr-sicht. Die tros-tet
mich und an-ders nicht. Ach myn-ne du hast
Eynen lie-ben wan ein
mir ge-ge-b(e)n. Sol ich an die vrou-we myn.
stren-giz le-b(e)n. doch din schilt ge-ver-te syn.

Jena, Universitätsbibliothek, Jenaer Liederhandschrift, f. 25.
*This note is missing in the manuscript in the first phrase but is present correct in the repeat.

And, toward the edges, stretching wide,
its wings are spread in hurried flight,
the shield is decked on either side
with coat of arms and colors bright.
Do you know her fame
and how she came
to us in word and body, too?
The infant there
cannot compare,
the glosses say that this is true.
Love, awaken,
firm, unshaken,
work, that all the mighty throng
thee may claim,
with dart and flame
and let us see who then is strong!
And truly, here comes Cupid flying,
torch, and bow and arrow plying.
His arrow pierces all attire

and then you, too, shall spread the fire.
A burning flame of joy and zest
has entered Cupid's seething breast.
Though he storms and rages wildly,
this is but a youthful sport,
thus one pictures him so childly.
He knows tricks of every sort.
He wears the crown
with a stately frown
who met and conquered many a king.
Give way, give way,
how strong his sway!
He overcomes each mortal thing.
Sees and kisses
pretty misses,
goes, but soon appears again.
If he chances
on loving glances,
Oh, he sends his arrow then.

Pity, Cupid, pity,
spare the young and pretty.
One small dart comes flying,
two with love are sighing,
ensnared by thee completely,
just for smiling sweetly.

Thou art in their land,
rage not with thy brand.
When breast to breast comes nigher
then kindles with desire
a flame upon the street,
thou burnest with great heat.

I regret thy blindness greatly,
for when cowards love too lately
then must Cupid act, and straightly.
Your game was ever blind and bare,
let others tell it if they care,
I'll say no more of this affair.

Wishing and dreaming
float as a feather,
thou guidest with scheming
high and nether.
Thy darts, brightly gleaming,
speed quickly and bring all lovers together.

Shield, relate thy story.
Thy field is red,
man for woman's glory
to pain is led,
the one is bruised and gory,
the other one is cold and dead.

Who the shield would carry
always must be merry,
although the infant strong
orders him to follow long
the song
which Paris brought us oversea,
stolen from the Spartan,
the love-sick swain to hearten.
Since the Greeks regained their prize,
who is fettered by love's ties
now cries
nothing but "Alas! Ah me!"

The *Leich* was related not only to the Latin sequence but also to dances such as the *estampie, ductia, stantipes,* and *nota.* The distinction between these dances is not clear, and it is possible that they were similar types of dances. They were all instrumental pieces, although the famous troubadour song "Kalenda maya" was a text improvised by Raimbaut de Vaqueyras to the *estampie* the musicians had just played, and Johannes de Grocheo speaks of singing the *ductia.* On many other occasions words were probably added to instrumental dance tunes.

The form used for the *estampie* was a series of sections, each usually consisting of a pair of phrases for which the music began alike but had different cadences. This strongly resembles the typical double-versicle segments of the *Leich.* Alexander's *Leich* is a somewhat more complicated form in which double versicles are mixed with through-composed sections. The basic scheme remains that of a series of connected songs with widely varying rhyme schemes, line lengths, and musical patterns.

This *Leich,* unlike that of Reinmar von Zweter (a religious *Leich*—see p. 125), has a secular text with vigorous dance-like rhythms in the poetry. Since the series principle was so familiar both in sacred Latin sequences and in secular instrumental dance tunes, it was quite natural for a secular form of the *Leich,* a dance *Leich,* to develop. The contrasting musical and poetic sections were probably danced in various ways. The style and tempo of the dance probably varied with the musical and poetic elements, for the short lines of the third segment of Alexander's *Leich* suggest a brisker, more lively movement than the longer, more stately lines of the fourth section.

Only the first four segments of the music of the *Leich* are given here, although the translation of the complete poem is given. The astonishing variety of musical forms may easily be seen even in this small segment; while the most common pattern is the double-versicle segment of the first and second parts, other arrangements are freely mixed with these. The form of the portion for which music is given is AA BB′ C DD EE DD FF. The C segment is through-composed.

Konrad von Würzburg

KONRAD VON WÜRZBURG was born sometime between 1220 and 1230 of middle-class parents in the city of Würzburg. He received a good education and was well read, not only in the German and Latin literature of his day, but also in classical literature. While still a young man, he moved to Strassburg and then to Basel, where he settled permanently. He died there in 1287.

Konrad was the first German poet-musician to support himself as an independent professional artist through performances and commissions. His patrons and clients were not nobles, but middle-class patricians and wealthy clergymen. He was very popular among his contemporaries and exerted a strong influence on his successors. Rumesland and Hermann Damen praised and imitated him, Frauenlob praised him highly, and the sixteenth-century meistersingers adopted him as one of the twelve Great Masters. This popularity was due, at least in part, to Konrad's versatility and productivity. In all, he composed some 85,000 lines of verse dealing with religious and secular material in epic and lyric form. He treated German and classical legends and sagas, and historical and contemporary themes. One of his longer works dealt with the Lohengrin saga, another with the Trojan War. His lyric works include nine summer songs, eleven winter songs, two dawn songs, a religious *Leich*, a dance *Leich*, and forty-four *Sprüche*, dealing chiefly with religious or political matters.

In his songs Konrad shows himself to be a master of language and a virtuoso of style. He was adept at coining words and obtaining variety of expression through synonyms. He employed alliteration and an enormous wealth of rhyme in his ceaseless search for originality of style and refinement of technique. Indeed, he often develops a highly complex pattern of initial, interior, and end rhyme which is quite impossible to translate. However, for all of his versatility and virtuosity, Konrad does not rank with the best of the minnesingers. He was a great craftsman, not a great artist.

Mir ist als ich niht lebende sî

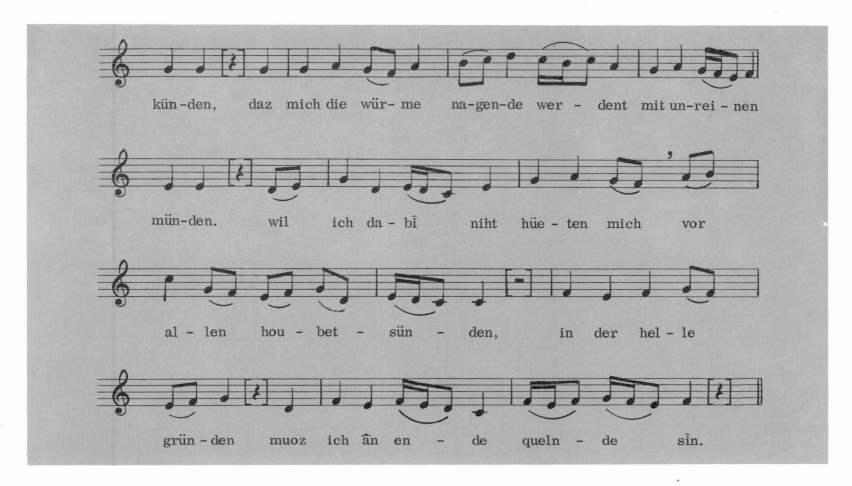

kün-den, daz mich die wür- me na-gen-de wer - dent mit un-rei - nen

mün-den. wil ich da - bî niht hüe - ten mich vor

al - len hou - bet - sün - den, in der hel - le

grün - den muoz ich ân en - de queln - de sîn.

Jena, Universitätsbibliothek, Jenaer Liederhandschrift, f. 100.

The text in the manuscript with the music is "Der nyt sin vas in dunkel verwet."

*This note is missing only in the first *Stollen*.

**This note is missing only in the second *Stollen*.

The small notes indicate those to be used for the repeat of the *Stollen*.

When I Begin To Drowse,
I Feel as if My Life Were Done

(*Mir ist als ich niht lebende sî, swenn ich entnücke sêre*)

The transitory nature of life and the omnipresence of death were favorite themes of Middle Latin verse. They were rarely treated by the noblemen among the minnesingers, but became more and more popular with middle-class singers. The music is that of another *Spruch* by Konrad which was composed in the same *Ton*.

When I begin to drowse, I feel   as if my life were done
and sleep becomes a symbol of   the death which I would shun.
With the setting sun
my shadow always teaches me
that life, like it, must fade;   And I'm reminded of the heat
of hell whenever in   the bathing house I take a seat.

Flowers tell how fleet
the gleam of transient joy can be.
In the mirror I can see   that I to dust must go,
and the charnal houses show
with their bones and smell
that worms will feed with unclean mouths   upon
   this mortal shell
If I do not abstain from sin,   then I shall later
   dwell
in the depths of hell
and suffer there eternally.

The many little embellishments in this song include a great many three-note figures and two five-note groups. Many interpretations could be used for these uneven divisions of the beat. The most common version is the one given here, with faster notes at the beginning of the beat. It would also be possible to sing the patterns as triplets and quintuplets. Either solution would be an approximation of a somewhat freer rendering of essentially ornamental figures. The same freedom would apply to the ornamentation of many of the other songs in this anthology.

Out of the Depths I Cry to Thee
(*Auss der dieffe schrei ich zu dir*)

The words to this song are not by Konrad, but by an unknown meistersinger who adapted the beginning lines of Psalm CXXX to a *Ton* and melody of the minnesinger.

Out of the depths I cry to Thee,
Lord, listen to my prayer,
my fear I cannot bear.
Bend Thy gracious ear
down to me, the voice now hear
of my pleading, oh God, my Grace.
Thy assistance give to me,
for, Lord, if Thou shouldst swear
no sinful man to spare,
oh then who would not fear.
For Thy mercy we revere
and honor Thee in every place.

I wait upon the Lord
adored,
that He may hear my soul.

Just as the minnesongs used older melodies with new words (contrafacts), the tunes of the minnesingers served as the basis for later songs. The meistersingers probably adapted minnesingers' tunes for their songs, although the models were undoubtedly changed greatly in the process. Some of the meistersingers' tunes may, in turn, have been adapted for church use, particularly during the Reformation, when the Lutherans used many secular tunes for chorales. One tune which could have been the model for a chorale is the psalm setting attributed to Konrad von Würzburg in the Berlin meistersinger manuscript. In this collection, the melody is dated in the thirteenth century. The chorale "Aus tiefer Noth," first published by Luther in 1524, begins with an identical phrase except for the mode. Since the subject of the psalm is the same as that of the chorale text, it is probable that the chorale is an adaptation of the earlier tune.

The transcription of Konrad von Würzburg's tune is in free rhythm. The *Blumen* at the ends of the phrases should be performed with great freedom by the singer.

May with Wondrous Skill
(*Manger wunne bilde*)

The difference between a genuine poet and an expert craftsman can readily be seen when one compares this summer song with one of Neidhart's or Walther's. Neidhart presents a lively and realistic situation, Walther portrays a real and personal emotion, but Konrad has only composed pretty and polished verses which are soon forgotten.

May with wondrous skill
in idle hours
created lovely things.
See, to vale and hill,
bedecked with flowers,
such a silken shimmer clings.

Auss der dieffe schrei ich zu dir

Auss der dief-fe schrei ich zu dir   O   Herr er-hör mein
Dein gne-di-ge hilff er-zeig mir   So   du Herr wilt im
D.C.Ich hof-fe auff sein wart a-lein   Auff   den Her-ren in

Sti-me   vor angst ich brin und gli-me   dein
gri-me   sünd zu rech-nen ver-ni-me   wer
que-le   war-tet al-zeit mein Se-le   von

gne-dig oh-ren   las merk-ken auff die Sti-me   für   bas
wirt be-stehn der   mas ist bei dir ver-ge-bung   auff   das
der mor-gen wach   rein biss zu an-dren stat gar   sein   —

mei-nes fle-hens o Got mein hort.
man dich Herr fürcht an al-lem ort.   Ich a-ber harr des
auff dich mein got ich hof-fe fort.

Her-ren Fer-ren   Er-hört er die Sel   mein.
    D. C. Stollen

Tübingen, Universitätsbibliothek, Depot der ehem. Preuss. Staatsbibliothek, Ms. germ. 25, f. 12.
The clef signs are incomplete in the manuscript.

Aus tiefer Noth

Martin Luther, 1523–24.

Luther's translation of Psalm CXXX in metrical style was written in 1523, and it is possible that the tune dates from the same year. The hymn was first published in 1524 when it appeared in Johann Walther's publications: *Etlich christlich lider Lobegesang* (Wittenberg), *Eyn Enchiridion oder eyn Handbüchlein* (Erfurt), and, in a contrapuntal setting, *Geystliches Gesangk Büchleyn* (Wittenberg).

Trees put on their clothes, behold
their crowns of leafy splendor!
Bird song, clear and tender:
a manifold
choir of forest voices sings.
Summer tide
doth provide
all the world with ecstasy.
What a wealth of joy has he
whose love is by his side.

May stills grief and pain,
and rich rewards
it bestows on hill and dale.
From the blooms a strain
of sweetest chords
comes from many a nightingale.
Violets blue and clover green
and daffodils of gold,
roses red unfold,
the fairest are seen
everywhere in wood and swale.
Summer tide
doth provide
all the world with ecstasy.
What a wealth of joy has he
whose love is by his side.

He, who at this time
doth love a maid,
and through such delights can stroll,
with a joy sublime
shall be repaid.
Love makes wounded hearts now whole.
Beauty for his eye appears
which apple blossoms bring,
and the birds all sing
to charm his ears.
Then shall love rejoice his soul.
Summer tide
shall provide
all the world with ecstasy.
What a wealth of joy has he
whose love is by his side.

Several texts have survived with refrains, but the music for all the minnesongs with refrains has been lost. German minnesong never used any of the complicated refrain forms (such as the *virelai*) of which the trouvères were so fond, but simple, probably choral, refrains were not uncommon in the summer dance songs, and are undoubtedly of very early German rather than Romance origin.

Robyn

THERE WERE apparently two minnesingers with the name Robyn or Rubin. One was a Tyrolean nobleman, a contemporary of Walther von der Vogelweide, the other was a commoner who lived one or two generations later. The *Spruch* below was composed by the latter, a singer who probably came from central Germany.

One Dare Not Greet with Praises
(*Nie man tzů vro sol prysen*)

"One dare not greet with praises
too soon the breaking day,"
thus spoke the ancient sages
long ago and plainly.
Splendidly may glow the morning
which later turns to gray,
perhaps with little warning,
and praise was given vainly.
Let singers then move slowly,
that honor be rightly meted,
to know the great man wholly
before their deeds are feted.
Praise won by actions lowly
is infamy repeated.

Robyn's song is unusual in that such care was used to designate not only the *b*-flats but also the *b*-naturals in the manuscript. They were needed to insure that the singer would not evade the diminished fifth and augmented fourth suggested in the melody of the first and second lines by adding *b*-flats (*musica ficta*). The Lydian mode, used in this song, is not very common in minnesong; so often do *b*-flats appear and with such consistency in the manuscripts that the mode is actually changed to F major.

Formally, Robyn's song is a *Barform* with a return of the complete *Stollen* melody at the end of the *Abgesang*. The B section is very short.

Nie man tzů vro sol prysen

Nie man tzů vro sol pry - sen mit lobe den liech-ten tac. Daz

han ich von den wi - sen. Lan-ge her vur - no-men. Luch-tet

her den mor-gen scho - ne. Dar - nach er tru-ben mac. vil -

lich-te vůr der nů - ne. Daz lob stet a - ne vro-men. So

sol man syn vůr - son - nen. Daz man mit sange icht to - be. Die

her-ren baz ir - ken - nen. E. man tzů vil ge - lo - be. Mit

vallsche eyn lob ge - wun - nen. Da sint tzwe las-ter o - be.

Jena, Universitätsbibliothek, Jenaer Liederhandschrift, f. 28.

Der Unverzagte

THE SINGER whose compositions appear under the pseudonym Der Unverzagte (The Undaunted) was a wandering knight whose language betrays a Middle German origin. Of his dates one can only say that he composed during the second half of the thirteenth century. Der Unverzagte was a *Spruch* poet whose twenty-two extant stanzas extol good breeding and morality, advise young people on virtuous conduct, and admonish the nobility with regard to their obligations as divinely appointed rulers and judges. He specifically avoids political or religious topics. His *Sprüche* appear in three different *Töne*.

The Good King Rudolph Loves His God
(*Der kuninc rodolp mynnet got*)

The hero of this *Spruch* was Rudolph I, a relatively obscure nobleman who founded the Hapsburg dynasty in Austria and was elected Emperor of the Holy Roman Empire in 1273. It is hard to say to what extent the song was intended to be ironical, for Rudolph was actually a very enlightened ruler for his day; on the other hand, he was known for his parsimony. It will be noted that the author mentions three different types of performance: singing, playing, and speaking. The "speaking" performance may refer to the recitation or chanting of long narrative works.

> The good King Rudolph loves his God   and is a
>   true believer,
> the good King Rudolph has renounced   the evils
>   which can hurt you,
> the good King Rudolph judges well,   abhorring
>   each deceiver,
> the good King Rudolph is indeed   a paragon of
>   virtue,
> the good King Rudolph honors God   and ladies
>   that are pretty,
> the good King Rudolph oft is seen   performing acts
>   of pity.
> I grant him gladly all the grace   his charity may
>   earn

Der kuninc rodolp mynnet got

Der ku-ninc ro-dolp myn-net got. und ist an tru-wen ste - te. Der
Der ku-ninc ro-dolp rich-tet wol. unde haz-zet val-sche re - te. Der

ku-ninc ro-dolp hat sich ma-ni — gen scan-den wol vůr - sa-get.
ku-ninc ro-dolp ist eyn helt an tugen-den un - vůr -

tza - get. Der ku-ninc ro - dolp e - ret got unde al - le wer - de

vrou-wen. Der ku-ninc ro - dolp let sich dicke in ho - en e - ren

scou-wen. Ich gan ym wol daz ym nach sy -ner mil - te heil ge - scicht. Der

meis-ter syn-gen. gi - gen. sa-gen. daz hort her gerne unde git yn drum-me nicht.

Jena, Universitätsbibliothek, Jenaer Liederhandschrift, f. 40.

who likes to hear the minstrels sing
and fiddle and speak and gives them naught in turn.

One of the best known of the later minnesinger tunes is this jaunty melody in F major. Its form is a modification of the *Barform* with return, with new material added for the last phrases:

$$\underbrace{\text{AA}'}_{\textit{Stollen}} \quad \underbrace{\text{AA}'}_{\textit{Stollen}} \quad \underbrace{\text{BB}' \quad \text{ACD.}}_{\textit{Abgesang}}$$

The construction of the *Stollen* and the first couplet of the *Abgesang* is reminiscent of the double-versicle construction of *Leich* segments. It is one of the freshest, most appealing of all the minnesinger tunes; it has been transcribed in both duple and triple meter by various scholars, but seems to assert its direct and vigorous character best in duple meter.

Whom Minnesingers Visit
Has Esteem and Reputation
(Swen gerende liute gerne suochent, der ist êren rîche)

Although a homeless minstrel, Der Unverzagte was proud of his profession and proud of his power, as the journalist and historian of his day, to make or destroy the reputations of kings and princes. This *Spruch* and five others were composed in the same *Ton* and to the same melody as the preceding song.

Whom minnesingers visit has   esteem and reputation,
whom minnesingers shun has faults   which bring
    him little fame,
whom minnesingers like to see,   he lives as fits his
    station,
whom minnesingers would avoid   deserves contempt
    and shame,
whom minnesingers love is one   on whom you can
    depend,
whom minnesingers hate is false   and would not
    help a friend.
whom minnesingers praise, beneath   a lucky star
    was born,
whom minnesingers curse has lost
his honor and shall reap disdain and scorn.

Learn Good Manners, Youth of Twenty
(Junger man von tzwenzich iaren)

Not only Der Unverzagte, but also many other singers from Walther on, felt a particular obligation to instruct the youth. Since their audiences at the court included many young pages who were learning the duties and skills of a knight, they had ample opportunity to do so.

Learn good manners, youth of twenty,
virtue brings reward in plenty,
love the Lord unceasingly is my advice.
Then your hopes will not deceive you
and your virtue will not leave you,
but protect you from the evils that entice.
Here a robe of constancy and chasteness wear,
heaven then will send you pleasures.
Honor women all as treasures,
so will you receive an angel's garment there.

Many of the songs of the Jena manuscript have highly embellished melodies. In almost all such songs, the melody of the second *Stollen* does not literally repeat the first *Stollen* but makes many small changes, from adding or subtracting up-beats to the lines to the addition of more elaborations of the line. Here one syllable and the note which goes with it is actually subtracted from the middle of the line, resulting in a shortened "measure."

Like many of the compositions of Der Unverzagte's contemporary, Hermann Damen, this song is distinguished by the number of melodic ornaments on weak beats. Songs with this characteristic seem well suited to transcription in duple meter, which allows time for an expressive rendering of the little melismas.

It Is an Art Which All Revere
(Ez ist ein lobeliche kunst)

This is one of the few poems which praises instrumental music and honors the instrumentalist as well as the vocalist. However, Der Unverzagte reflects the general opinion of his day in ranking song above strings, even though he, as well as the other minnesingers, was an instrumentalist and his own accompanist. The poet

Junger man von tzwenzich iaren

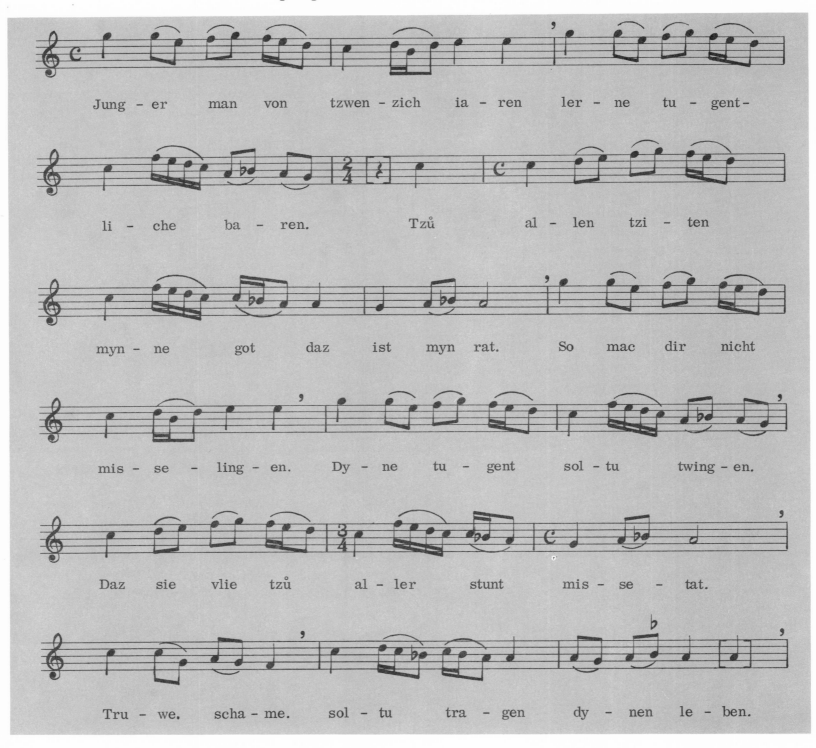

Jung - er man von tzwen - zich ia - ren ler - ne tu - gent-

li - che ba - ren. Tzů al - len tzi - ten

myn - ne got daz ist myn rat. So mac dir nicht

mis - se - ling - en. Dy - ne tu - gent sol - tu twing - en.

Daz sie vlie tzů al - ler stunt mis - se - tat.

Tru - we. scha - me. sol - tu tra - gen dy - nen le - ben.

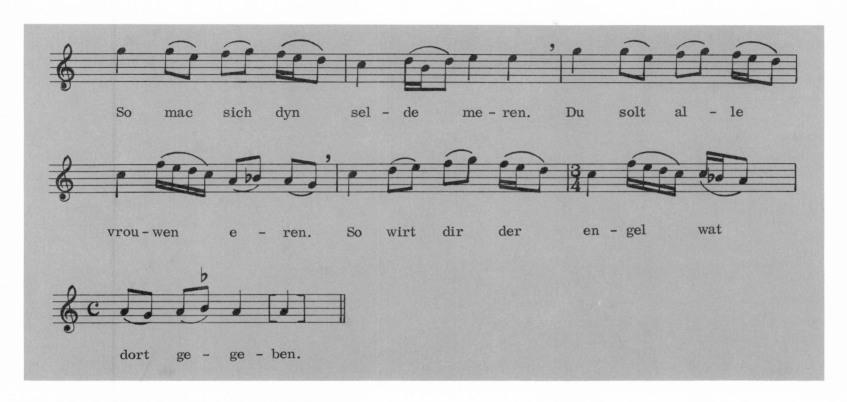

So mac sich dyn sel - de me - ren. Du solt al - le

vrou - wen e - ren. So wirt dir der en - gel wat

dort ge - ge - ben.

Jena, Universitätsbibliothek, Jenaer Liederhandschrift, f. 39.

reminds his listeners of the time-honored doctrine of the curative powers of music, which the medieval world inherited from the Greeks.

> It is an art which all revere
> to play well on a fiddle's strings;
> the fiddler makes our spirits light,
> but song shall have my praises here.
> Song teaches women, men, and kings,
> song makes God's table still more bright.

> To song the sounds of strings belong,
> who loves them more than minnesong
> will have to do without my praises.
> Song can be writ in words and phrases
> to cure the world of its malaises.

The transcription is in free rhythm. For some of the cadences, a double note used in the manuscript has been interpreted as an indication of a lengthened note value, and is shown by a half note in the transcription.

Ez ist ein lobeliche kunst

Jena, Universitätsbibliothek, Jenaer Liederhandschrift, f. 40.

The small notes indicate those to be used for the repeat of the *Stollen*.

Hermann Damen

HERMANN DAMEN was a singer from northern Germany, the son of a respected citizen of Rostock. He composed his songs during the last quarter of the thirteenth century and the first decade of the fourteenth century. From him we have one *Leich* and a number of shorter works, mainly *Sprüche*. He was a teacher of the famous Frauenlob, whom he mentions in one of his songs.

Damen's compositions do not differ greatly from those of other middle-class singers of his time. His work is chiefly of a didactic and religious nature and his style is characterized by an occasional tour de force of rhyme. Sometimes the same rhyme is used in four or five consecutive lines, sometimes the rhyming words may be as many as ten lines removed from each other.

Would the World but Show Me Kindness
(*Het ich al der werlde hulde*)

The simplicity of form of this song offers a pleasant contrast to Damen's usual style. The unrhymed line, called an "orphan," was borrowed by the early minnesingers from Provençal song. Five other *Sprüche* dealing with similar themes were written in this *Ton*.

> Would the world but show me kindness,
> then what joy would I possess.
> God forgive them for their blindness
> who would steal my happiness.
> I know such knaves, and do not love them,
> those who envy all good people
> and can say but evil of them.

This tiny song uses a *Barform* with a return of the complete *Stollen* melody after only a very short B section at the beginning of the *Abgesang*. It has been transcribed in duple time to show the effect of this meter on the little ornamentations on weak syllables which are so characteristic of Hermann Damen's tunes. The only change in the last appearance of the *Stollen* melody is that the last note is repeated and thus lengthened.

Het ich al der werlde hulde

Jena, Universitätsbibliothek, Jenaer Liederhandschrift, f. 117.

To Grace This Melody I Brought
(Ich male of des sanges symz)

This song illustrates in two ways the decadence of the late minnesong. In the first place, it shows art turned in upon itself: it is a poem about poetry. In the second place, the use of rhyme is highly pretentious (every tenth line rhymes), revealing the skill of the poet without contributing anything to the ear of the listener. The first line of the song is interesting in that it adds further evidence to the theory that the minnesingers often put words to tunes, rather than the reverse.

To grace this melody I brought
the fairest words I could devise,
but you must help to brighten
gloomy darkness in my verse.
You thus shall give me aid
and earn the other poets' praise.

So weave with thought the charm of verse within
   your heart
and they'll commend you gently.
I shall also honor you,
for I am heartily afraid that ever
my art may weigh still less than thought
when measured with another's prize.
The judging scales will heighten
the fame of one, condemn the worse
and show us where was made
an error or an awkward phrase,
that one may see and form a perfect work of art,
whose words are blended stately
with the tune and meter too.
The song shall then bring praises for endeavor.
It honors man,
exalts the wives,
gives wisdom for tomorrow.

Ich male of des sanges symz

man unde wir – det wib. Ouch git er ho-e le – re. Swer syn vil

kan. vil ma – ni-gen lib. vryt er von sene(n)-der swe – re. Sanc ist der

kunst eym ge-spie-gelt trymz. Swer syn da kun-de ie ge-

wan. Der liez sich tugen-de vie – ren. Nach prises si-te

of itz-lich ort. Da von stet al myn gir. Dar-

nach daz ich ge-rech-ten sanc. vil gerne_ir – kan – de.

wiz – zent daz swer sy – nen kranz. So birt daz

er vůr gra- ze. Sy - ne tzun-gen hat be – hůt. Der

treyt yn daz er ym nicht wirt tzů swe - re.

Jena, Universitätsbiblothek, Jenaer Liederhandschrift, f. 123.

*The flat is missing in the second *Stollen* of the manuscript.

The small notes indicate those to be used for the repeat of the *Stollen*.

The singer can
give many lives
relief from pain and sorrow.
For song the splendor of art has wrought,
and he who masters song shall rise
to fame, and praise shall lighten
his heart, and all his cares disperse.
In this my hopes are laid,
that I may rightly form my lays.
Whoever wears the crown of song and will impart
its verse and tune sedately,
singing nothing he may rue,
shall wear it long and find it weighty never.

The length of the first section of this poem is such that the complete A A B A form of the melody is a real *da capo* form. The repeats are almost literal, with only occasional discrepancies in ornamental notes. The musical form faithfully reflects the rhyme scheme, for it not only repeats the sections whose rhymes repeat, but the sound *e-re* is always found with the same kind of melodic figure, whether it is in the A or B section of the poem (the interval is changed in the B section, but the figure remains basically the same).

I Shall Sing Thy Love Excelling
(*Eyn lob syng ich dir tzu prise*)

Damen's pleasure in the manipulation of rhyme is especially noticeable in this song. In addition to thrice repeated end rhyme, he adds, in the fourteenth and final lines, initial rhyme. Initial rhyme does not begin with Damen, but goes back at least as far as Rudolph von Fenis. Damen composed nine *Sprüche* in this *Ton*.

I shall sing Thy love excelling,
in my song Thy praises telling,
so that I may share Thy dwelling
when life has its ending.
Never shall his guile disarm me,
who would lie in wait to harm me,
neither shall his hate alarm me
with my Lord defending.
I shall not be his prey,
my allegiance he shall never gain,
and he shall have no pay
for his toil but everlasting pain.
Thou Three-in-One, transcending,
sending down the word that frees us

Eyn lob syng ich dir tzu prise

Sende uns dy - ne ho - en le - re. Durch al

di - ner tu - gent e - re. of daz sich un-

heil uns ve - re her - re heil uns sen - de.

Jena, Universitätsbibliothek, Jenaer Liederhandschrift, f. 121.

*The manuscript has  in the first *Stollen* and in the second *Stollen*.

dy - ne spi-se   of mich sa - chet

**In the manuscript, the *b* is missing in the second *Stollen*.

from the evil which would seize us,
through the love that seeks to please us,
Jesus, save unending.

Songs in which the melismas fall mainly on the weak syllables could be transcribed in duple meter, but they also work well in the second rhythmic mode (with each measure short-long). In such a transcription the melismas will fall on the long part of the measure, producing, in the case of this song, a very convincing effect. This is one of the very few minnesinger melodies which can be transcribed effectively in this mode. The form of the song is:

ABCD   ABCD   EFEFGABC'D'.
Stollen   *Stollen*   *Abgesang*

The mode is Dorian.

The Dissolution
of the Minnesong

Frauenlob

HEINRICH VON MEISSEN, better known as Frauenlob, was born about 1260, probably in or near the city of Meissen. Nothing is known of his parents except that they were not of the nobility. Frauenlob attained local distinction as a singer at an early age and left the city when about fifteen to begin his career. He traveled first to the south. In 1278 he was with the army of King Rudolph of Austria and was the chief performer at a large festival during which the king knighted the young squires who had been serving at his court. In 1292 Frauenlob was in Bohemia and sang on the occasion of the knighting of King Wenzel II. A few years later he was in Carinthia, the southeastern part of present-day Austria. His wanderings then took him to the north, to Brandenburg, Mecklenburg, Bremen, and Denmark. In these states he sang at various important festivals and was treated more as an honored guest than as an entertainer. About 1312 he went to the city of Mainz as the most famous minnesinger of his day and remained there, probably under the sponsorship of Archbishop Peter von Aspelt, until his death. Legend, supported by an engraving on his tombstone, says that Frauenlob's casket was carried to its resting place by eight beautiful girls. He is buried at the Cathedral of Mainz, but the exact spot is no longer known.

The most characteristic features of Frauenlob's art are the result of his philosophic and pietistic inclinations. He was familiar with the principal tenets of Scholasticism, which saw the moral and physical world as a uniform representation of divine wisdom. The omnipresence of divine reason became the central factor in Frauenlob's thinking and therefore the traditional words and concepts of chivalry, as he uses them, have new meanings and values. His concept of *minne* is different from that of his predecessors and becomes a rather abstract virtue. Sometimes it means married love, a divine necessity for society; sometimes it has a spiritual significance, becoming a love of divinity, or a guide to knowledge of divinity.

Frauenlob composed three *Leiche,* thirteen minnesongs, and about 450 stanzas of *Sprüche.* His verse is characterized by a lively fantasy, by a baroque playing with words, pictures, and parables, and by vague, not readily comprehensible concepts. His similes and meta-

Myn vroud ist gar czugangyn, nu horit iamirliche clag

sich - te.   Mich hilft nicht vrey ge - mu - te,   noch kun - de - keyt, noch

o - byr - müt,   noch al - lir   vrou-wyn gu - te.   Myn tognt, myn kraft, myn

syn - nyn,   das ist al - lis gar - vor - lorn;   der mich czu ge - sel - lin

hot dyr korn, das ist der tot,   myt dem mus ich von hyn - nyn.

Vienna, Nationalbibliothek, Hs. 2701, f. 17.
"Das ist vrouwinlobis in der grünen wyse."

phors, when not biblical, are more often drawn from middle-class life than from that of the nobility. The meistersingers mistakenly celebrated Frauenlob as the founder of the first of their singing schools.

My Joys, Alas, Have Vanished,
Now Hear This Sorrowful Lament
(Myn vroud ist gar czugangyn,   nu horit iamirliche clag)

Most of Frauenlob's *Sprüche* appear in groups of three, which can be presented as three-stanza songs. The *Sprüche* below were probably composed shortly before the minne-singer's death. Indeed, he may have known at the time of composition that he was dying.

My joys, alas, have vanished,   now hear this
    sorrowful lament:
I rue the sore offenses   with which my days on
    earth were spent.
Often have I gone astray,
now death will take me and the world forget me.
My life will soon be over,   since death my early
    end has sworn;
whatever gifts I offer,   all are lost and I must mourn,
for he will summon me away;
alas, the haunting fears that now beset me!
No cheerful heart can save me,
nor wisdom, nor can haughtiness,   nor love the ladies
    gave me.

My virtue, strength, endeavour:
all are lost and I must mourn.
Who chose my company forlorn
is fearful death; with him I leave forever.

Now death would tear asunder   my life and me,
  and thus am I
so overcome with sorrow.   Oh God, in mercy hear
  my cry.
Receive my soul, my body may
again to earth and to the worms be given.
My art, my poet's spirit   will fade within my heart's
  confine;
Oh, who may these inherit,   for they can be no
  longer mine,
God giveth and He takes away;
may I receive the joys for which I've striven!
My songs I'll sing no longer,
now hear these words of deep distress,   death waxes
  ever stronger,
now heed my warning surely:
I speak to men and ladies all,
since each a prey to death must fall,
to righteousness hold fast and keep securely.

Maria, spotless mother,   because of thy beloved son
remember me in mercy.   And Thou, whose pain
  redemption won
on the cross where all might view
the bloody spear which pierced Thy side, O Savior.
It was a Jew who thrust it,   but Thou forgave his
  wicked deed,
and so I pray Thee, Master,   because of Thy
  distress and need
when Thou wert wounded by the Jew,
because of all Thy pain show me Thy favor.
Oh weep, ye eyes once merry!
Sir Death, what canst thou want with me?   My
  tears will help to bury
poor Frauenlob in flowing,
for bitter death my end hath willed.
Oh God, why must this voice be stilled?
So let it be, and few will mark my going.

The repeat of the *Stollen* adds some ornaments and places up-beats on different phrases. At the end of the *Abgesang* the last phrase of the *Stollen* is repeated. It is interesting to note that the same expressive melisma is used on the word *tot* (death) which occurs in the same place in both the first *Stollen* and the last line of the *Abgesang*.

The same song appears in variant versions in a number of other sources: the Jena manuscript (with the words "Wer kante gotes krefte") and the Donaueschingen, Colmar, and Adam Puschman's songbooks (with the text "Her Simeon der wise"). The Jena version is the most highly ornamented one, while most of the ornaments were removed in the other three, which are largely meister-singer sources.

I Hear My Father's Proverb Say, "Child if You Would See"
(Ich hore des vater lere ihen.   kynt wiltu sen)

Although Frauenlob, like Walther von der Vogelweide, often gave advice specifically to the rulers of the German states, unlike the latter he did not advocate particular courses of action, but confined himself to general matters of policy and behavior. His tendency to use words in a broadly symbolic manner is illustrated in this *Spruch* by the references to the "door" and the "flood of life."

I hear my father's proverb say, "Child, if you would
  see
value in yourself, then let this be.
The less of grief, the more of fear;
keep long within your heart the words which now
  you hear,
thus you can seek the counsel that you need."
You princes must be cautious, too;
who comes to you
not by the door, his counsel is not true.
Have both your thumbs right in your hands;
be careful whom you trust with honor, power, and
  lands.
I see straight through
the honied stratagems and greed.

Ich hore des vater lere ihen. kynt wiltu sen

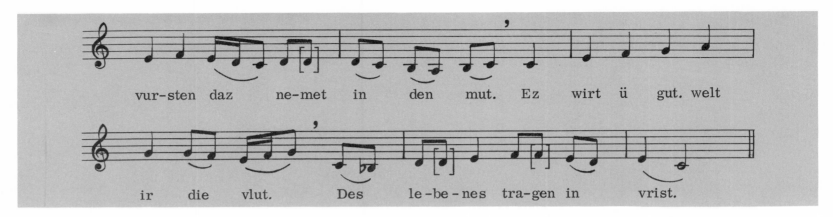

vur-sten daz ne-met in den mut. Ez wirt ü gut. welt

ir die vlut. Des le-be-nes tra-gen in vrist.

Jena, Universitätsbibliothek, Jenaer Liederhandschrift, f. 110.
The small note indicates that to be used in the second *Stollen*.

One marks how often fortune's stay is brief,
how bliss can change to pain without relief
and joy can end in grief.
These truths, you princes, recognize,
if you'd be wise
and would arise
the flood of life to lead.

Like many of the songs of the Jena manuscript, a casual use of unaccented syllables occurs throughout this song. In the first line an extra note is supplied for the extra syllable and is left out on the repeat of the *Stollen* when it is no longer needed. Most of the time, however, the extra syllables are simply placed in the space between the notes in the manuscript, and the singer was obviously supposed to repeat the note, dividing the time, so that no more beats would be added for the extra syllable. In one place in this song, at the end of the third phrase, a neume is to be divided for *sehen,* but on the repeat of the *Stollen* the same neume is to be sung slurred on one syllable.

The last phrase of the *Abgesang* uses the same music as the last phrase of the *Stollen*.

Lo, I Saw a Maiden
(*Ey ich sach in dem trone*)

These are the first two segments of Frauenlob's most famous work, *The Lay of Our Lady*. The first segment forms a song which in its simplicity of form and content resembles the folk song. The second segment is complex in structure and its language is rather symbolic and abstract. It consists of two stanzas in which rhyme within the individual stanzas appears and also rhyme between corresponding lines of both stanzas. In the latter case the rhyme words are ten lines apart. The question at once arises as to whether such rhyming was merely a game which the author played for his own amusement or was actually an effective poetic device. It is possible that Frauenlob's audiences were more accustomed to long-delayed rhyme than we are and that their hearing was more retentive than is ours.

I

Lo, I saw a maiden
with child upon a throne,
her crown was heavy laden
with many a precious stone.
She wished to be delivered,
the best of maidens said;
a dozen diamonds quivered
and sparkled on her head.

II

When nature's course was run,
the lovely one
brought forth a child, a wondrous son,
in labor, as another.

Ey ich sach in dem trone

Munich, Staatsbibliothek, Cod. germ. 4997, f. 19 (the Colmar manuscript).

Her wisdom first could see
that he
with seven lamps was there.
She saw him then arise
a lamb before her view
on Zion's mountain peak.

She did all that she could,
the sweet and good,
and bore the flower of field and wood.
if you became the mother
of lamb or peaceful dove
of love,
O maidens, you would swear
('twould be no great surprise)
such food would bring to you
the fruit for which you seek.

Frauenlob's *Marienleich,* "Ey ich sach in dem trone," follows the principle of the double versicle more rigourously than the other *Leiche* of this anthology. Here every section makes a literal repeat, even to the same cadence, so that for the forty-four sections of the poem, there are exactly twenty-two different melodies. It was well known in its own time and is found in five manuscripts.[1] The most important are the Colmar manuscript, on which this transcription is based, and the Vienna manuscript (Vienna, Nationalbibliothek, Hs. 2701), in which unfortunately the beginning is missing. In the Colmar manuscript it is described as "unser frawen leich oder der guldin flügel zu Latin Cantica Canticorum" (the *Leich* of our Lady or the golden wing of the Latin Song of Songs).

The first two sections of the music are given here. It is interesting to note the echo effect employed for the short rhyming lines, in which the same music is repeated for the rhyming syllables:

Nu merkent wie *sie truge*
die gefuge

. . . .

Den nach sie vor *ir sitzen*
mit witzen

The transcription is in modal rhythm with most of the feminine phrase endings lengthened to $\downarrow. \mid \downarrow$.

[1]Linker lists the following manuscripts: The Colmar manuscript (Munich, Staatsbibliothek, Cod. germ. 4997); Munich fragment M (Munich, Staatsbibliothek, Cgm, 5249/32); Wroclaw, Biblioteka Universytecka, Ms. I. Q. 368; Königsberg fragment (Königsberg, Universitätsbibliothek 7); Vienna, Nationalbibliothek, Hs. 2701. Robert White Linker, *Music of the Minnesinger and Early Meistersinger* (Chapel Hill, University of North Carolina Press, 1961), p. 5.

Wizlaw von Rügen

WIZLAW III, the last prince of the Slavic family which had ruled over the Baltic island of Rügen and the neighboring mainland since their Christianization, was born about the year 1268. The family was closely related to other ruling houses of the north. The singer's mother was a daughter of the Duke of Braunschweig-Lüneburg, his brother, Jaromar, became the ruler of the bishopric of Kammin, a sister became Queen of Norway, and a nephew became Duke of Pomerania. After the death of his father in 1302 Wizlaw shared the throne with his brother, Sambor, until the latter's death two years later, at which time he became the sole ruler of the principality. His reign was a troubled one. He was threatened on the one hand by the rising power of his largest city, Stralsund, and on the other by the territorial ambitions of Denmark to the west and Brandenburg to the south. After years of internal and foreign war an unsettled peace was established and Wizlaw devoted his final years to the building up of his impoverished and war-torn land. He died in 1325 and left no heir. Rügen was ruled for a time by the Duke of Pomerania, but soon both lands were swallowed up by Brandenburg.

Wizlaw, according to one account, was "a knightly gentleman, a politician of dubious talents and an even worse financier." He was interested in science and the arts and associated much with scholars and poets, among whom was Frauenlob, one of whose songs praises the noble character of the prince. Fourteen minnesongs and thirteen *Sprüche* by Wizlaw are extant. The *Sprüche* are chiefly concerned with moral and religious matters and may have been influenced by Reinmar von Zweter. They were probably composed before the minnesongs. The latter are much superior and represent a sort of Indian summer of the classical minnesong.

Wizlaw's characteristic note in the minnesongs is an optimistic and happy one. Although he sang of love's sorrows as well as its joys, his pain is always lightened by hope and never approaches despair. He sings of the joys of love in a frankly sensual manner which sometimes recalls that of Walther von der Vogelweide. There is charm in the best of Wizlaw's verse even for the modern reader; however, his music is generally superior to his verse and

Meyie scone kum io tzǔ

Jena, Universitätsbibliothek, Jenaer Liederhandschrift, f. 78.

*The manuscript has ♭♭♭ here in the second *Stollen*.

belongs to the best which the German minnesong has produced.

Come to Us, Delightful May
(*Meyie scone kum io tzŭ*)

Most of Wizlaw's minnesongs are preceded by a nature introduction which frequently is carried through most of the song. The stanzas are more closely tied together than are those of the majority of the minnesingers. Indeed, in this song the rhyme is continued from stanza to stanza by the device of rhyming the final word of one stanza with the initial word of the following stanza.

Come to us, delightful May,
long have you remained away,
asleep.
The women wear such dreary clothes,
this is chief among my woes.
They keep
all their pretty dresses from the weather,
but you, fair May, can change this altogether.
They're hidden by the coats they wear
(Winter, this is most unfair)
from cold.

Hold, oh Winter, frosts that chill
and I'll be your vassal still.
Forbear!
It's a fault you cannot hide,
making us remain inside.
I share
all the heavy trials that you measure,
but I am silenced by a single pleasure.
It's the long and happy nights
with their amorous delights
so dear.

Here I stay and shall not go,
for my lady's winsome glow
makes me
happy as a blissful boy.
God, take not away this joy,
I beg Thee.

When she gently calls and I awaken
my every member then with joy is shaken
and I exclaim: "Oh rosy lips,
how my heart with rapture skips!
God bless you."

A modal rhythm has been chosen for this transcription, although either duple or triple meter could be used.

With My Faithfulness Would I Adorn Thee
(*Ic parrêre dî dorch mîne trôwe*)

It has been suggested that some of Wizlaw's minnesongs were composed for his first wife, Margarete. One is tempted to think that this one may have been. The verses are Wizlaw's best and contain a depth of warm and personal feeling such as seldom appeared in the minnesong.

Although Wizlaw's songs are extant only in a High German version, it is generally assumed that they were originally composed in the language of his north German homeland. The text which here accompanies the music of the song is a reconstruction of the Low German original.

With my faithfulness would I adorn thee,
since my eyes first saw thee in thy beauty.
Love, be mine, and never let me mourn thee,
thou paragon of virtue and of duty.
Oh none can merit thy affection
save God who grants thee His protection;
this I too must have or soon must perish
of love for thee whom I would hold and cherish.

Both "Ic parrêre dî dorch mîne trôwe" and the following song, "Wol uph ir stolzen helde," have been transcribed in duple meter. Occasional lines of irregular length cause some changes in the placement of bar lines, but do not cause a real change in the flow of duple units.

Ye Youths in Fancy Feather
(*Wol uph ir stolzen helde*)

In spite of the slightly pretentious repetition of rhyme, there is a simplicity of rhythm and structure in this song

Ic parrêre dî dorch mîne trôwe

Jena, Universitätsbibliothek, Jenaer Liederhandschrift, f. 75.

Text reconstruction, Margarete Lang, *Ostdeutscher Minnesang* (Lindau, Kostanz, Thorbecke, 1958), p. 62.

which is not far removed from that of the folk song. Indeed, if one were to omit the last two lines of each group of four rhyming lines, one would have a form and rhythm which sometimes were used in the popular peasant songs of the fifteenth and sixteenth centuries. The fact that the author in the last stanza refers to himself as "Wizlaw, the Younger" makes it clear that the song was composed before the death of his father, Wizlaw II.

> Ye youths in fancy feather,
> come, let us go together
> to fields of blooming heather,
> for wondrous is the weather,
> and hear him not who scolds.
> Their springtime splendor wearing,
> their branches outward flaring,
> the trees are now preparing
> for songbirds, homeward faring,
> the charm of May unfolds.
> Then hasten to the fields and sing along
> with the birds their sweetest melody,
> and with the May win beauty from the song
> for your lives,
> and from tender, loving wives.
> The May to us has given
> a life of sorrows shriven.
> We gain, by honor driven,
> the joy for which we've striven.
> Our thanks, oh May, to thee.

> The May has come in splendor,
> the birds a welcome render,
> and breezes, soft and tender,
> mark winter's full surrender;
> May's beauty now we sing.
> Our song of praise embraces
> also the ladies' graces,
> if May were dead, their faces
> and lovely gowns and laces
> would make another spring.
> But now we have both ladies and the Maytime,
> May shall bring us joy and naught shall grieve us
> while we sing and dance through night and daytime

> once again.
> Therefore, ladies, join the men!
> My wise command obeying,
> do what your heart is saying,
> come now, without delaying,
> to where the music's playing,
> before the May shall leave us.

> Woman, how you torment me,
> when you could so content me
> and such delights present me,
> but, no, away you sent me—
> alas, that I must tell it.
> How oft your lover raises
> his voice to sing your praises
> in sweetest notes and phrases,
> but, though his passion blazes,
> you give him naught to quell it.
> What's that within your heart I cannot capture,
> that will not let you give your love to me?
> You are my shrine of bliss, my dream of rapture,
> you, my sweet,
> alone can make my joy complete.
> Wizlaw, the Younger, is singing
> this song. His lady is bringing
> him sorrow—bitter and stinging.
> But hope is ever springing:
> how glad that day will be!

In this song the repeat of the melody of the *Stollen* at the end of the *Abgesang* is freely varied. The frequent use of the *b*-flat gives the song a strongly Phrygian character.

Lovers Who Together Lie
(*List du in der minne dro*)

This is a fragment of a conventional dawn song. The first four lines of the first stanza are missing from the manuscript, which begins with the song of the watchman on his round. He warns the lovers of the approach of day.

> "Lovers who together lie,
> it lightens in the eastern sky,
> the birds all greet the morn: day is nigh."

Wol uph ir stolzen helde

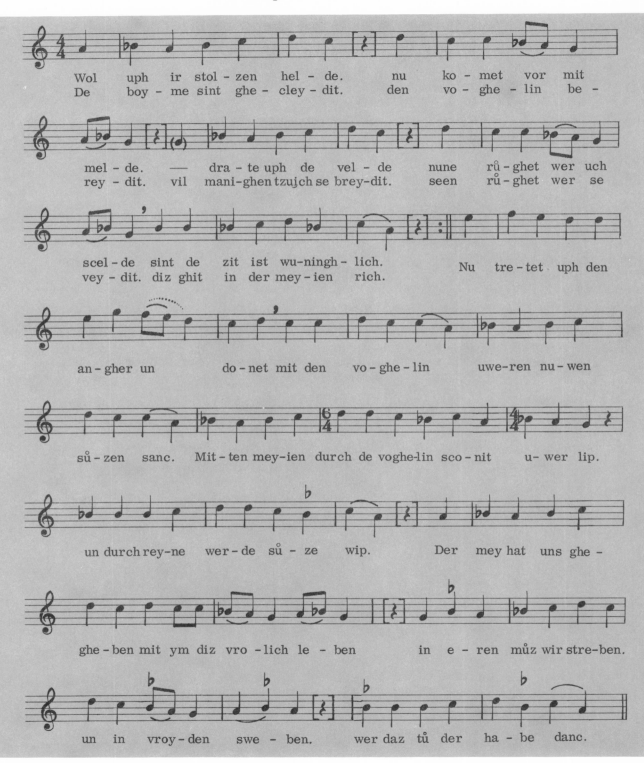

List du in der minne dro

List du in der min - ne dro.------------ Ich

se den lech - ten mor-ghen vro.--------- de voghelin singhen den

tac. Her ist----------- ho.----------------------------

Jena, Universitätsbibliothek, Jenaer Liederhandschrift, f. 77.

This caused the knight to sorrow,
he woke the lady pale:
"My love, I'll come tomorrow—
my darling—without fail."
She threw her arms around the knight
in great distress and held him tight,
but he caressed her till her heart was light.

In deepest grief they parted,
the lady was in tears.
He swore before he started
that she need have no fears.
But all his efforts were in vain,
she cried to him, "My love, remain!"
He said, "I'll soon come back again."

Some of Wizlaw's songs have so many melismas that
the possibility that some of them were instrumental interludes has been suggested. In "List du in der minne dro,"
however, the melismas are used to imitate the sound of
birds mentioned in the text. This device is used also in
the famous bird song of Oswald von Wolkenstein, "Der
may mit lieber zal" (see p. 221), and it appears frequently
in Renaissance music, but the only other minnesinger
before Wolkenstein who employs it is the Monk of Salzburg (see pp. 192 and 196).

In this transcription each neume has been made equal
in value.

The music is incomplete in the manuscript, surviving
for only the last part of the first stanza. No indication is
given as to how the succeeding stanza texts are to be set
to the melismas of the last line, which refers to birds only
in the first stanza.

The Fields and Forests, Far and Near
(Der walt un angher lyt ghebreyt)

Of particular interest in this song is the skillful manner
in which variations in the metrics of a line, produced by
the substitution of dactyls and spondees for iambs, are
emphasized by the use of initial rhyme. In the original

Der walt un angher lyt ghebreyt

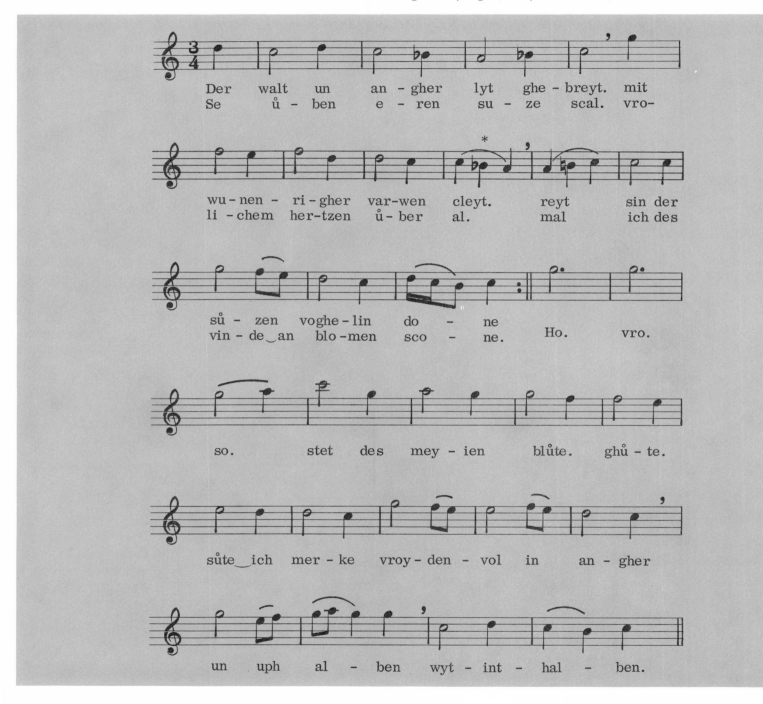

Jena, Universitätsbibliothek, Jenaer Liederhandschrift, f. 79.
*The flat is missing in the second *Stollen*.

Wizlaw was surprisingly successful in combining direct and natural expression with a highly involved rhyme and rhythm pattern.

> The fields and forests, far and near,
> in brightly colored dress appear.
> Hear   the sweet notes from leafy bowers,
> the birds are singing a pretty air
> with happy spirits everywhere.
> Fair   is the sight of trees and flowers,
> clear,   dear,   sincere   are the Maytime's faces.
> Graces,   places
> of charm I see with joy o'er hills and meadows
>   wending,
> far extending.

> The wonders of the fields in May
> are fair as on creation's day.
> They   can't compare with a new creation,
> that drives away each pain and sigh,
> a lovely lady, sweet and shy.
> I   see in her my true salvation,
> sight,   might,   delight,   all on me bestowing.
> Glowing,   showing
> kindness to me, oh darling, my love you must
>   cherish,
> else I shall perish.

> Oh Love, your bounty is so great
> that I could die from this joyful state.
> Fate   has made you my well of gladness
> and I am wholly in your power:
> grant me many a happy hour,
> shower   with blessings, banish sadness.
> Your name   and fame   I proclaim,   knowing I
>   shall never,
> ever   endeavor
> to part from that which frees from care and brings
>   me bliss.
> Wizlaw, sing this!

Wizlaw's sensitivity to the melodic qualities of vowel sounds was reflected in the extended melismas in some of his songs. In this one, however, he emphasizes the sonorous qualities of the vowels *o* and *u* by using one-word rhyming lines with distinctive melodic devices. At the beginning of the *Abgesang*, the repeated *g* for *Ho. vro. so* suggests that each note be lengthened to produce a spondaic rhythm. On the words *blute. ghute. sute* he uses a sighing figure which is part of a five-measure descending sequence. Both these groups of sounds are emphasized if the transcription is modal, although for all Wizlaw's songs either a duple or a triple meter is tenable. The initial rhyme with which the last line of each *Stollen* begins is also emphasized by lengthening the note in the transcription.

I Weighed My Plight
(*We ich han ghedacht*)

The metrical pattern of dimeter and trimeter lines is so characteristic of gay summer songs that it inevitably lends a careless, joking mood to this lament. Wizlaw's expressions also give some support to the suspicion that he does not intend for his sorrow to be taken too seriously.

> I weighed my plight
> throughout the night
> and my most sad ambition,
> which a woman wrought
> who had no thought
> to bring it to fruition.
> I hoped to see and greet her.
> A little kiss
> from her lips is bliss,
> I know of nothing sweeter.

> For shame, my sweet,
> are you discreet,
> that you should want to harm him
> who love would find
> and thinks you kind?
> Why don't you try to charm him?
> I counsel you to render
> a token of
> your faithful love
> as proof your heart is tender.

We ich han ghedacht

We ich han ghe - dacht al di - sen
De eyn wyp be - ghat. un mich nicht

nacht. an mi - ne gro - zen swe - re.
lat. ko - men tzů ey - ner we - re.

Daz se mir wol - de na -

hen. Eyn cus - se - lin. uz ir munt ist

phin. den wolde ich wol unt - pha - hen.

Jena, Universitätsbibliothek, Jenaer Liederhandschrift, f. 77.

The songs I sing
can never bring
to me your true affection.
I suffer pain
and only gain
my death with your rejection.
But still my prayers continue.
We cannot part,
my foolish heart
must ever strive to win you.

The folk-like simplicity of the tune is well suited to the jaunty meter in which the text is set. The same melodic figure is used for all the dimeter lines, producing the form:

AAB   AAB   CAAB
Stollen *Stollen* *Abgesang*

The use of the *b*-flat gives a Phrygian flavor to the mode.

The Monk of Salzburg

ALTHOUGH nearly a hundred songs appear in some fifty different manuscripts under the name of the Monk of Salzburg, his identity has not been definitely established. It is most plausible to assume that he was a Prior Hermann who was attached to the Benedictine monastery in Salzburg in the early fifteenth century. In any case the composer of the songs was a member of the circle of poets and musicians which gathered at the court of Archbishop Pilgrim II von Puchheim (1365–96) in Salzburg. There are over forty religious songs and nearly sixty secular songs extant. The former are largely adaptations of Latin hymns, the latter are for the most part in the courtly minnesong tradition, but some show a definite affinity to the folk song.

The courtly minnesongs of the Monk are characterized by a baroque playing with form, by highly complicated structural patterns and rhyme schemes. Especially well known are his harvest songs, in which he describes the St. Martin festivities in language much like that of Neidhart. Also like Neidhart are his descriptions of the physical charms of the beloved one.

Most of the melodies to the Monk's songs have been preserved. A reference in one of the manuscripts to a lay priest by the name of Martin who helped the Monk with the songs has raised the possibility that Hermann may have composed the verse and Martin the music.

O Lady, Dearest to My Sight

(*Zart libste frau in liber acht*)

The two chief tendencies of the minnesong in the fifteenth century, toward the sterile and mechanical craftsmanship of the meistersong on the one hand and the simplicity of the folk song on the other, are both seen in this song. The first two lines with even tetrameter could have introduced a folk song, but then enjambment and parenthesis produce lines like those of the meistersong.

Oh lady, dearest to my sight,
wish me a pleasant, joyous night,
thy loyalty gives such delight
and ever leads my steps aright

Das nachthorn, und ist gut zu blasen.

Zart libste frau in liber acht

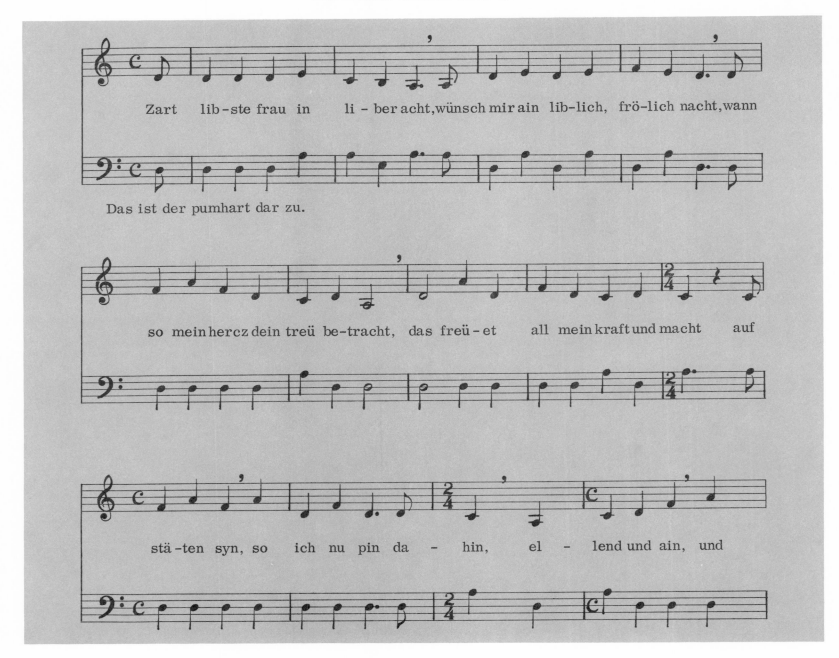

Zart lib-ste frau in li – ber acht, wünsch mir ain lib-lich, frö-lich nacht, wann

Das ist der pumhart dar zu.

so mein hercz dein treü be-tracht, das freü-et all mein kraft und macht auf

stä-ten syn, so ich nu pin da – hin, el – lend und ain, und

Vienna, Nationalbibliothek, Hs. 2856, ff. 185, 186.

when I'm away,
as now, that they
not stray.
I'm all alone
with none my own
to comfort me
but thee.
My longing drives away all sleep,
and see,
the whole night long for thee
I weep.
Sweet dreams such happiness supply
and always make me wish that I,
waking never,
might sleep forever
with pleasant dreams that never end.

Four of the Monk of Salzburg's pieces in the Mondsee-Wiener manuscript bear the names of instruments. The first three are "horn" songs: *das nachthorn* (the night-horn), *das taghorn* (the day-horn), and *das kchühorn* (the cow-horn). The fourth is called *die trumpet*. The first two and the fourth are described as *gut zu blasen* (good to play on wind instruments) and apparently could even be played by instruments alone, the first (and last) time such a suggestion appears in the history of the minnesong. The names may specify the kind of instrument which is to play them, or they may possibly be the names of traditional tunes or patterns associated with those instruments. The three different names for the horns probably refer to their uses rather than to different kinds of instruments.

Just which instrument was specified by the term *horn* in connection with these pieces is also a matter for debate. Watchman, hunters, soldiers, and shepherds of the late Middle Ages used short, wide-bore horns which probably sounded signals on a single note or on the fundamental and the first two overtones, which would not have sufficed to play these melodies. Some longer, narrower horns are depicted in the later Middle Ages, but these still could not have played these pieces. However, from the tenth century on, pictures appear of an animal-horn with a few fingerholes, a precursor of the late medieval *cornett* (*Zink* in German), which was an instrument with a horn mouthpiece and fingerholes. Shepherds in remote parts of Sweden still use such an instrument, made of cow-horn. Such an instrument could have played the notes of the Monk's horn pieces easily, and with its bright, clear tone could also have accompanied voices. The term might also mean one of the other instruments played by watchmen and tower musicians, which by the fourteenth century included shawms (ancestors of the modern oboe, woodwind instruments with conical bore and double reed) and trumpets, those hitherto royal instruments whose use was among the new privileges being accorded to the towns. Tower musicians were usually wind players only, but the Limburg Chronicle of 1370 describes performances by singers accompanied by winds from the town tower. They may well have performed music like these songs of the Monk of Salzburg.

"Das nachthorn" ("Zart libste frau in liber acht") is notated with two parts, one with text and the other a purely instrumental part for the *pumhart*. This instrument, also known as the bombarde, was the bass member of the shawm family. The simple accompaniment which it plays may be a clue to the kinds of parts instruments could improvise when nothing was written for them. It is an alternation of tonic and dominant (*d* and *a*) with two *e*'s and an *f* at one cadence point. The melody it accompanies is very simple and instrumental in character. It could only have been played with an instrument with fingerholes, such as the *cornett* (*Zink*) or a smaller shawm. The accompaniment is entirely note-against-note.

From Deep and Gentle Sleep
(*Gar leis in senfter weis*)

Although the song is not without poetic feeling, it gives the impression of a rhyming crossword puzzle rather than of a poem. Caught up in the tour de force of rhyme, one can easily forget the girl of whom the Monk is singing. The lack of rhyme in the last line creates an effective element of surprise.

From deep
and gentle sleep,
my love, arise
and turn your eyes
to skies
where starlight flies
and darkly lies
the heaven's blue.
Awake, my charming maid, that you
in passion sweet
may greet
your heart, which dwells in me.
Your voice will be
a melody to me
and thrill

me, if you will
but wish a fond "Good day."
Your glances say,
with many a gleaming
love-light beaming,
that your affections I possess.
My heart then leaps with happiness
and hope that my reward is near,
your eyes have promised me, my dear;
till it appear,
may I receive a greeting from your lips.

"Das taghorn" ("Gar leis in senfter weis") is no less a musical than a poetic tour de force. It is built entirely from notes of the overtone series (the third, fourth, fifth, and seventh partials above the fundamental *c*—*c'*, *e'*, *g'*, and *c''*) except for several *a*'s, which although outside the series could have been produced by stopping the horn to lower the sixth partial (normally a somewhat flat *b*-flat). It could, therefore, have been played on some type of natural horn or trumpet.

Very interesting instructions are given for the performance of the piece: "Das taghorn, auch gut zu blasen, und ist sein pumhart dy erst note und yr ünderoctava slecht hin." This could be translated "The day horn, also good for playing on a wind instrument, and the first note and its underoctave throughout is for the *pumhart*." This rubric is rather ambiguous: it could refer either to a doubling of the melody in octaves by the *pumhart,* or, as is much more likely, to a drone part beginning on the octave below the first note of the melody and held throughout the piece. Drone instruments such as bagpipes and the drone string on the vielles were probably widely used throughout the period, but this is one of the few explicit references to the use of a drone in a particular piece.

The *horn* referred to may have been an actual horn, although it is generally believed that the medieval horn could not play such high harmonics, or a trumpet, which by the fourteenth century had developed a considerable skill in the use of upper partials. Trumpets of this period apparently were also equipped with a sliding section which could have shortened the length of the tube to produce the

Das taghorn, auch gut zu blasen, und ist sein pumhart dy erst note und yr ünderoctava slecht hin.

Gar leis in senfter weis

pir   der stymm von   dir,   (Instrumental)

daz mir gar still dein rai-ner will wünsch li – ben   gu – ten   tag,

den   mir   hëut   sag   tu-gent-li–chen myn-nik-li – chen dein

güt mit man–gem li–ben   plik,   so daz mein hercz in frëu-den

schrik zu trost der lib–sten zu–ver–sicht,   der   mir dein

weib–lich   güt ver – jieht,   bis   das   ge – schicht,

daz   mir wünsch gu–ten   tag dein   mund.

Vienna, Nationalbibliothek, Hs. 2856, f. 186.

a's required by the piece. If it was not played as an instrumental piece alone, an instrument was still required for the introduction and interlude which appear without text.

Listen, Dearest Lady, to My Plight
(Hör, libste frau, mich deinen knecht!)

In this composition the traditional alternating song has become a dialogue which is accompanied by the continuous song of the watchman. Such an ensemble work, although containing many elements of the minnesong, has exceeded the limits of the genre and should preferably be called a polytextual polyphonic song.

(the lovers)
Listen, dearest lady, to my plight.
—What is all this long harangue at night?
—I only wish you, lady, well.
—Speak, what do you have to tell?
—What my longing heart befell.
—This desire that you pursue . . .
—Is, my dear, to be with you.
—Do not sorrow,
come tomorrow.
—Lady, stay!
—Why not come to me by day?
—What will evil gossips say?
—Nights they're watching all around.
—I stole here without a sound.
—Whisper low
what I'm to know.
—Joy and grief have filled my heart.
—Can't you tell the two apart?
—Grief is pain, but joy is nice.
—I can give you good advice.
—Do so, lady, counsel me.
—You must practice loyalty.

(the watchman)
I warn you both to flee,
honestly,
as I should,

for I only want your mutual good.
Who has honor, he has care,
I advise you to beware,
bliss the gossips cannot bear.
This is what I warn you of,
for when love is seeking love
it must fear their spite,
for their evil words can bite
as do deadly snakes.
See what pride the poisonous gossip takes
in his evil ways:
he brays
like an ass
of the honor of his class,
he'll surpass
all in boorish brass,
for he wants the rest to be
just as mean and low as he.
He indeed
swaggers when his wiles succeed.

The polyphonic pieces are all in mensural notation, so there is no doubt about the interpretation of the rhythms in this piece. The performance instructions are detailed. The upper part, or at least the introduction to the upper part, is labeled "This is called the trumpet and is good to play on a wind instrument." The introduction and much of the song could be played by a trumpet. In the upper part of the song, after the trumpet's introduction, the knight's part is written in black and the lady's in red, producing a dialogue song with two different singers. Monophonic dialogue songs were probably sung by a single singer who switched his point of view in assuming each role; here, however, the manuscript indicates that two singers play the roles. The dialogue song is accompanied by a watchman's song for a third singer.

To the Fairest, Sweetest One Who Lives
(Dem allerlibsten, schönsten weib)

This minnesong takes the traditional form of the love letter or *salut*. There are several other stanzas, the last of which gives the date, 1392, and identifies the sender of

Hör, libste frau, mich deinen knecht!

(He)   (She)

hal-den dich   O, wy ge - ren ich das tät! Pis vor al -len din - gen stät.

tu-gent lër,   als   er   ist: des frëut sich sein fal -scher list.

Vienna, Nationalbibliothek, Hs. 2856, ff. 188, 189.

the letter as "Pilgrim." Although this certainly refers to Archbishop Pilgrim II, it probably does not mean that he composed the song. The name of the town, Freudensal, means "Hall of Joy" and is obviously an allusion to Neidhart's castle of Reuenthal.

To the fairest, sweetest one who lives
in Freudensal, Dame Honor Bright,
I send this little note, which gives
the best regards that I can write.
Source of all the joys I've sought,
know this, my heart and every thought
are sore distraught,
my days are long and bring me naught.
No one on earth is half so fine,

I like each way and worth of thine:
the path of honor thou didst choose,
such was thy nature and design.
No woman would I rather see.

Like many of the songs of Montfort, those of the Monk include several melismas which are probably instrumental preludes, interludes, and postludes. Such instrumental sections may well have been improvised for many of the songs of other minnesingers, even though they were not explicitly called for. "Dem allerlibsten, schönsten weib" begins and ends with such passages but has no interludes. The notation is interesting since many of the phrases end with doubled notes, which indicates that they are to be lengthened, probably to double value.

Dem allerlibsten, schönsten weib

(Instrumental) Dem al – ler-lib- sten, schön-sten weib im

Frëu-den-sal, frau e – ren gail, send ich den brif, dar – an ich schreib meinn

dinst, ge – lük und al-lez hail. Zärt – li -cher freu-den A-ne-vank, wizz,

daz mein hercz und mein ge-dank an a – be-gank sich sent,daz mir dy

weil ist lank; wann mensch auf erd ward ny so zart, mich frëu vil paz dein

weis und wart: du pist, frau, auf der e – ren pfat ge – wön-lich ko-men

und von art: ny weib ge-sach ich ger – ner zwar. (Instrumental)

Hugo von Montfort

COUNT HUGO VIII of Montfort-Bregenz and Tannen-berg was a highly respected and influential nobleman with extensive estates scattered throughout Austria. He was born in the year 1357 in the Voralberg region near the present borders of Germany and Switzerland. As a boy he was a page at the Viennese court where, in addition to learning the manners and duties of a knight, he was instructed in the art of the minnesong. At the age of sixteen he entered into the first of three apparently happy and certainly very profitable marriages. In later years he distinguished himself as a soldier in a crusade against the heathen Prussians, in a campaign in Italy, and in various engagements in defense of his outlying estates against Swiss and Bohemian encroachments. In the service of Duke Leopold of Hapsburg he proved himself an able diplomat and statesman, for which he received many honors. He died in 1423.

Forty poems appear in manuscripts under Montfort's name, but the authenticity of two has been questioned. His compositions include *Sprüche,* minnesongs, and letters in verse. Montfort breathed new life and vigor into the minnesong, or, one might say, he changed it into something different and more modern. His earliest songs are conventional, but, as a mature artist, he produced contemporary compositions which reflected personal feelings and experiences, revealed the manners and mores of his own time, and had little to do with outworn traditions. Although clearly the work of an intelligent and educated man, they stand closer to the folk songs of his day than to the classical minnesong. They were composed in the few leisure hours of a busy life, some of them on horseback as Montfort rode from one to another of his estates.

Montfort did not compose his own melodies, but depended for them on a vassal, Burk Mangolt. It was probably not unusual for a minnesinger, particularly one who was a wealthy nobleman, to employ a composer for his songs; however, that he should freely admit this and give due credit to the composer is unique in the history of minnesong and speaks much for Montfort's honesty.

Ich fröw mich gen des abentz kunft

sy mich nit die rain die zart

(Instrumental) So wär ich

gar ain hür - nin man.

Heidelberg, Univ. Bibl., Cod. Pal. germ. 329, f. 10.

*The manuscript has a misplaced clef sign for the line beginning at this point and ending with *vernunft*, causing it to read a third lower in the original.

**Through an error in the placement of the clef signs, the original is notated a third lower from this point to the end of the piece.

At Evening I Await Alone

(Ich fröw mich gen des abentz kunft)

This dawn song is an early one and fairly traditional in content. The simplicity of Montfort's metrics here offers a welcome relief from the virtuosity of his immediate predecessors and gives the song a more personal flavor.

At evening I await alone
the night, when she will steal to me,
and so will make her favor known;
my hopes are high as they can be
that she her kindness will reveal.
Had I no pleasure in such charm,
I'd be a man of brass or steel.

The church bell brings us sweet distress
and then I hear the watchman's horn;
we share a kiss, a fond caress,
for we must part with breaking morn.
Such parting is a grievance sore,

but, if I thought I'd not return,
then I would sorrow even more.

With us decorum must prevail
and modesty our love restrain,
should someone tell another tale,
then would it cause us woe and pain.
Now Jupiter and Venus pale,
they flee before the rising sun,
the day has come to wood and dale.

Despite the fact that in the manuscript the first syllable of the text is set under the beginning of the long melismas of the melody, they are probably instrumental interludes and a prelude. No rhythmic indications appear in the manuscript of this song, but the melodic structure of the melisma is in every case a variation of the phrase which follows. The rhythm of the transcription is a modal triple meter. The ornamented phrases are transcribed using the basic rhythmic structure of the unadorned version, to

Mich straft ein wachter des morgens frü

(Instrumental) Mich straft ein wach - ter des

mor - gens frü Er sprach wenn wilt du ha - ben ruw (Instrumental)

Din sin - gen a - be - lan Lie - der tich - ten tu nit mer (Instrumental)

Das rat ich dir by mi - ner er Da - von man tan - tzen tut (Instrumental)

Wach - ter des wil ich vol - gen dir Der

lied ge - ticht ich nie - mer mir (Instrumental) Des solt du si - cher

sin Suss müss ich lo - ben sel - ge weib (Instrumental) Die sind der

welt doch ... laid-ver-treib Ach gott wie lieb und zart (Instrumental)

Ich welt wer fro-wen ... ü-bel sprech Das

man in durch die zun-gen stech (Instrumental) ... Das la-ster musst er han.

Heidelberg, Univ. Bibl., Cod. Pal. germ. 329, f. 11.

which the neighboring-tone figures and other embellishments are added.

At Dawn a Watchman Was Scolding Me
(*Mich straft ein wachter des morgens frü*)

The liberties which Montfort took with the traditional forms of the minnesong are well illustrated in this song. Although it contains the person of a watchman and is composed as a dialogue, it is not a dawn song and has nothing to do with the parting of lovers. It also breaks with tradition in that it does not sing the praises of a particular lady-love, but is a eulogy of all women, both wives and sweethearts. The recurrent unrhymed lines show the influence of the folk song.

At dawn a watchman was scolding me:
"When will you ever rest," said he,
"and let this singing end?
Write no more songs upon your scroll,
is my advice upon my soul,

to which the people dance."
"Watchman, your words I'll not ignore,
such dancing songs I'll sing no more,
of this you may be sure.
But lovely women I must praise,
they brighten life's distressing days,
My God, how dear they are!
And he who ill of them has sung,
were I to say, would lose his tongue,
and he'd deserve such shame.

"Watchman, now mark and judge their worth,
whatever I have seen on earth
is but an idle breeze
compared to the love of wife, or maid,
here neither art nor sense can aid,
and this was always true.
David, even Solomon,
Samson, too, was once undone,
he lost his life complete.
Therein did women have a part,

a virgin broke the seal of art.
Away, you ladies sweet!
Whoever women shall offend
will come to no congenial end.
They like not scorn or blame.

"Watchman, look at the firmament,
the day comes from the orient,
I hear the song of birds.
All blessed women may it wake,
May God protect them for His sake
from every traitor's tongue.
Who loves and tells is most unkind
and, though with seeing eyes, is blind,
he can't endure for long.
The roses all that I have seen,
the blossoms, all the foilage green
are but a jest to me
compared with lovely maidens' charm
with graceful bearing, glances warm,
God grant them blissful days."

The long melismas within and between the phrases of Mangolt's tunes are the subject of much controversy. The most generally accepted view is that those between or at the beginning of phrases are instrumental passages. Those in "Mich straft ein wachter des morgens frü" do not elaborate on the following phrase like those of the preceding song, but use new melodic material.

Jammers, however, believes that all the melismas were vocal in character and were meant to be sung.[2] It certainly would be possible to vocalize them on the syllable of the first word of the phrase, although the instrumental interpretation seems most satisfying musically.

If they were played by an instrument, the instrument probably continued to accompany the singer either at the unison or with a decorated or simplified version of the same line.

Tell Me, Watchman, of the Morn
(Sag an wachter wie was es tag)

Here Montfort uses the form of the dawn song to sing of the wonder of creation. The poem has three stanzas, but parts of the final two are missing in the manuscript. The unrhymed lines have caused the question to be raised as to whether the songs were altered in transmission. This could easily be possible, for Montfort spoke a different dialect than that of the manuscript. However, since the poet himself said that he was a poor rhymer, it should be assumed that the lines were originally unrhymed.

Tell me, watchman, of the morn
before the earth and sky were born,
before there were the elements and planets.
Then neither sun nor man made light,
but God in majesty and might
was there, who has no end and no beginning.
The word is God, and God the word;
all things were made when it was heard
and all were fair according to their nature.

Mangolt's musical forms are often more sophisticated than those of his immediate predecessors. Even though he uses standard forms, he uses them as guiding principles rather than formulas to be filled in. This is in striking contrast to the later rigid use of forms by the meistersingers. In "Sag an wachter wie was es tag" the form is:

$\underbrace{ABC}$	$\underbrace{AB'C'}$	$\underbrace{DB''C''}$
Stollen	*Stollen*	*Abgesang*

The varied return of the second and third parts of the *Stollen* at the end of the *Abgesang* is changed even more by the insertion of an interlude between the last two phrases which did not appear in either *Stollen*. Though this does not appear in other minnesongs, it may indicate one of the ways in which instrumental interludes, not written by the composer or compiler, were improvised by the performers in other songs. Details of this kind are of particular interest in the case of this manuscript since it dates from near the time the composer lived, and thus is perhaps closer to the original form of the songs than some other minnesong remains.

---

[2]Ewald Jammers, "Die Melodien Hugos von Montfort," *Archiv für Musikwissenschaft*, XIII (1956), 217–35.

Sag an wachter wie was es tag

(Instrumental)   Sag   an   wach-ter   wie

was es   tag do   hi - mel und erd   nit   em - phlag pla-

ne - ten zwar   und   auch die   e - le - men - ten.

(Instrumental)   Da   luch - tet   we - der

sunn noch man gott waz   in der ma - ie - stat   vil schon ge-

wal - tig   ye   und   ist noch e - wenk - li - chen gott

ist das wort das wort ist gott da - mit ge - macht an

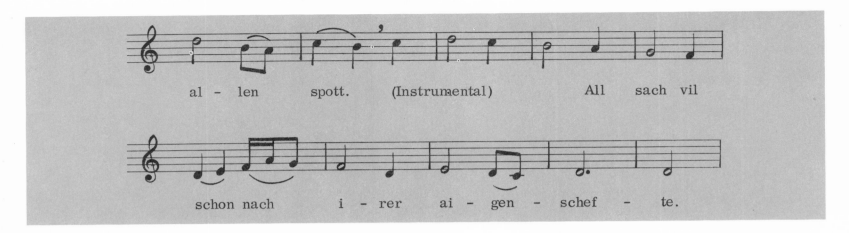

al - len   spott.   (Instrumental)   All   sach   vil

schon nach   i - rer   ai - gen - schef - te.

Heidelberg, Univ. Bibl., Cod. Pal. germ. 329, f. 12.

*The manuscript has

Dame World, You Are So Sweet and Fair
(*Fro welt ir sint gar hüpsch und schön*)

This is the first stanza of a long poem written, as subsequent stanzas intimate, at the time of the death of Montfort's second wife, in 1401. It is an alternating song in which the singer declares his intention of renouncing worldly pleasures and Dame World attempts to dissuade him. Each stanza is divided equally between the two antagonists. Such arguments between a man on the one hand and Dame World, Lady Venus, or a pagan spirit on the other became popular in folk ballads. One of this type of folk ballad was adapted by Goethe for his famous "Erlkönig" song. Montfort's description of Dame World as a beautiful woman behind whom all sorts of evil lurk is repeated in many paintings of his time.

"Dame World, you are so sweet and fair,
but your reward's destruction.
Your loving words and lilting air
are magic of seduction.
Whoe'er devotes himself to you
is soon misled and straying

and at his end has much to rue.
I've often heard this saying."
"Dearest companion, why this blame?
I gave thee courage, gave thee graces,
and yet must reap reproach and shame.
Come learn of joy in my embraces,
leave care to the birds and live with me
and merrily dance each night instead
(with this advice I counsel thee),
a crown of roses on thy head."

The notation of this manuscript includes a sign which could have a rhythmic meaning in some of the songs—a stem added to the note. In "Fro welt ir sint gar hüpsch und schön" the stem seems to have two uses; sometimes it appears only on the highest note of the phrase and sometimes it is used for every note of the phrase. Runge's transcriptions of the songs treat it as a plica, a type of ornamental note.[3] As this interpretation produces an ungainly

[3]Paul Runge, *Die Lieder des Hugo von Montfort mit den Melodien des Burk Mangolt* (Leipzig, Breitkopf & Härtel, 1906), p. 45.

Fro welt ir sint gar hüpsch und schön

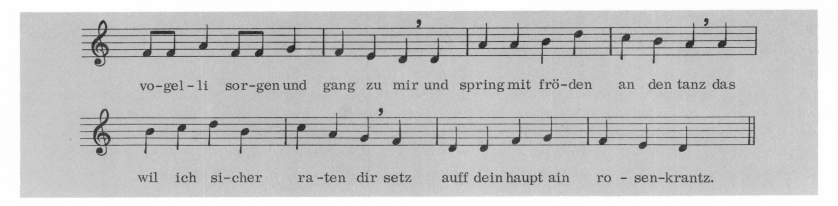

vo-gel-li sor-gen und gang zu mir und spring mit frö-den an den tanz das

wil ich si-cher ra-ten dir setz auff dein haupt ain ro - sen-krantz.

Heidelberg, Univ. Bibl., Cod. Pal. germ. 329, f. 35.

*The manuscript has

melodic line, it has not been used in this transcription. Though in some of the other songs it does seem possible that it could mean a lengthened note, no such consistent pattern seems to govern its use in this song; the present transcription ascribes to it no rhythmic or melodic significance in this case. Wolf suggests that some such signs may be survivals of the note form of the virga and that they have no specific rhythmic implication.[4]

The musical form of the song is unusual—

$$\underbrace{\text{AB\quad AB\quad CDEF}}_{\text{The Poet}}\qquad\underbrace{\text{GHIJ\quad G′HI′J′}}_{\text{Dame World}}$$

—and reflects the dialogue structure of the text. In the repeated sections there are a number of notes which do not exactly correspond. The second line appears to contain an error, in which the five notes at the beginning of the line are notated a step too low, but the other differences may have been intentional (the up-beat of lines 9 and 13, the last notes of lines 11 and 15, and the first three notes of lines 12 and 16).

Four lines end with light syllables for which an extra note was provided in the manuscript; notes are also provided for the extra light syllables of line 13. Succeeding stanzas do not consistently require these extra notes and indeed sometimes have extra syllables in other places.

Wake, Awaken, Lovely Sleeper
(*Weka wekh die zarten lieben*)

This is the first stanza of a four-stanza song which was composed in praise of the poet's third wife. Montfort's independence of tradition is seen in his use of the form of a dawn song, previously employed to tell only of stolen love, to compose this warm and personal testimony to his marital happiness.

"Wake, awaken, lovely sleeper!"
I think it not unrightly done,
I wish not to deceive her,
the day begins to dawn.
In truth, she lingers never,
the waker of my heart's desire,
her pleasure waxes ever
in service of her God.
Whoever has a loyal wife,
he has a treasure-trove of bliss.
Her praise and honor cheer his life.
I hear the songs of birds,
I watch the starlight leave us,
I feel the cool of early morn,
but find that not so grievous.
Her face makes all so fair.

[4]Wolf, *Handbuch der Notationskunde*, I, 177.

Weka wekh die zarten lieben

We – ka wekh die zar – ten lie – ben Ich glaub es sey nicht

un – recht tân Ich wil ir nit be – trie – gen

Der tag der gat da – her Si stat zwar auff mit

e – ren Meins her-tzen mut er – ki – ke – rinn Ir glükch das

tut sich me – ren Ze dinst dem wer – den gott Wer hat auff

erd ain bi – derb weib Der hat ain sel – den – rei – chen hort Ir

zucht ir er ist laid – ver – treib Ich hör der vo – gel sang

Heidelberg, Univ. Bibl., Cod. Pal. germ. 329, f. 46.

In a few cases, such as "Weka wekh die zarten lieben," Jammers thinks that the stem indicates a lengthened note.[5] It is often found on unaccented syllables. The transcription in this anthology treats the basic rhythm as a triple modal meter, with each note having a stem lengthened, the amount of the lengthening being determined by the context.[6] The lengthened note on the penultimate syllable is indicated in the manuscript by a doubled note.

The song is also interesting in its use of a three-note melodic figure at the beginning and freely through the piece which imitates the call of the watchman at dawn.

Throughout the song previously used motives reappear in freely varied combinations.

[5] Jammers, *loc. cit.*
[6] Wolf, *loc. cit.,* suggests that such a stem might show a weak syllable without necessarily involving a rhythmic change.

Watchman's call

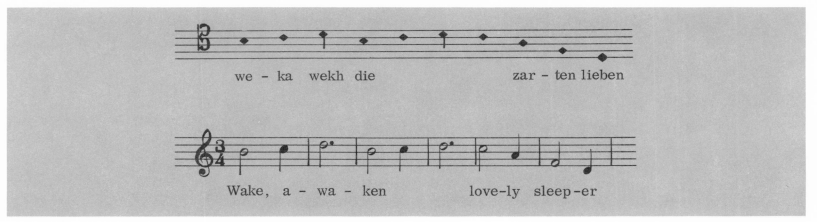

Oswald von Wolkenstein

OSWALD VON WOLKENSTEIN was one of the most dynamic, colorful, and ruthless figures in the history of German verse and music. He was born in 1377 as the second son of a wealthy and powerful knight of the southern Tyrol, an area which, though German-speaking, is now a part of Italy. Wolkenstein's adventures began when he left home at the age of ten, probably in the service of a German knight, to begin prolonged wanderings throughout the Near East and the lands surrounding the Mediterranean. He was absent for about thirteen years, during which time he learned, as one song relates, ten languages. When his father died, Wolkenstein returned home to share the inheritance with his two brothers. Since all three were of a headstrong and avaricious nature, the sharing was accomplished only after some theft, violence, and even bloodshed; however, the brothers were not permanently estranged from one another.

A second but shorter period of wandering began for Wolkenstein in 1415 when he entered the service of King Sigmund of Hungary. At this time he traveled first to Spain and Portugal, where he took part in a battle, later to France and Italy, and finally to England and Scotland. In 1417 Wolkenstein returned home and was thereafter only infrequently absent from his homeland. This does not mean, however, that he settled down to a life of quiet domesticity. In 1418 he took part in an unsuccessful revolt againt Duke Friedrich of Austria and soon afterwards a property dispute which he had carried on for years with another noble family became violent. In 1421 Wolkenstein was lured into the hands of his enemies by a woman and was imprisoned. Eventually Duke Friedrich intervened in the dispute, but was not able to arrange any settlement; Wolkenstein, however, was set free. Six years later he was imprisoned again, this time by the duke, and a final settlement of the property dispute was made. The settlement was not unfavorable to Wolkenstein, although he seems to have had no legitimate claim to the property he had seized. In his later years Wolkenstein became more and more influential in Tyrolean affairs, but he remained quite ruthless in his attempts to increase his holdings at the expense of others and without recourse to law. He remained vigorous and ambitious till his death in 1445.

Zer - gan - gen ist meins her - zen we, seit das nu flies - sen
Er - wa - chet sind der er - den tünst, des me - ren sich die

wil der sne, ab Seu - ser al - ben und auss Flack, hort ich dem Mos-mair
was - ser - rünst, von Kas-tell - rut in den I - sack, das wil mir wol be-

sa - gen. Ich hör die vog - lin gross und klain in
ha - gen. Auff von dem ut hoch in das la und

mai - nem wald umb Hau - en - stain die mu - sik pre - chen
hrab zu tal schon auff das fa durch ma - nig süe - sse

in der kel, durch scharp-fe nöt-lin schel - len.
stimm so hel, des freut euch guet ge - sel - len. Was

Ob

get die red den Plät-scher an? mein sin - gen mag ich nit ge - lan. wem
mir dir vai - gen sein ge - var noch tröst ich mich der frum-men zwar. wie

das miss-vall, der lass mich gan, und sei mir heur als verd.
wol das heu-er an dem jar valsch pö - se münz hat werd.

Since the chief manuscripts which contain Wolkenstein's songs were prepared under his personal supervision, it is probable that all or nearly all of his compositions have been preserved. They comprise 127 poems, some quite long, and 124 melodies. The songs consist mainly of love songs, autobiographical songs, and moral or religious songs. They are chiefly characterized by the strong impression of immediate experience which they give. His love songs have little to do with the courtly concept of *minne*. One feels that they tell of real women whom the singer knew and of actual relationships with them. The autobiographical songs, too, have an unmistakable aura of authenticity and are commonly accepted as true history. The moral and religious songs, which were perhaps composed during Wolkenstein's imprisonments, also reveal a background of actual experience, but the sentiments expressed in them are rather formal and shallow in comparison with his other works. Wolkenstein reveals no depth or sincerity of moral or religious feeling.

A second and equally important characteristic of the songs of Wolkenstein's early and middle life is the remarkable unity which they achieve. In his best works melody, verse structure, rhythm, language, and content are adapted to each other with astonishing success. However, Wolkenstein's compositions show a wide range of merit, and the poorer ones have little but technical proficiency to recommend them. It is only a short step from the later works of Wolkenstein to the uninspired and mechanical productions of meistersingers.

Departed Is My Bosom's Woe
(*Zergangen ist meins herzen we*)

This is the first stanza and the refrain of a spring song. The stanza is sung by the minnesinger, the refrain by two birds in turn. Mosmair was a farmer friend of Oswald von Wolkenstein; the Isack is a river which flows by Hauenstein; the other proper nouns are place names. The song was probably composed between 1417 and 1421.

Departed is my bosom's woe,
since ice begins to melt and flow
from Seuser hills and down from Flack;
so I heard Mosmair say.

The mists of earth have been released
the springs and streamlets have increased
from Kastelrut to the Isack;
this makes my spirits gay.
The birds within these woods of mine
which lie near Castle Hauenstein
pour forth sweet music from their throats
with happy heart and voice.
From *do* the song goes up to *la*
and down again to trill with *fa*
and sharp and clear are all the notes,
so, feathered friends, rejoice.
"What is this gossiper below
who interrupts my singing so?
If it offends him, let him go;
it's all the same to me."
"Although his voice cause us to fear,
I trust the one who sounds sincere;
it's well that counterfeit this year
can still demand a fee."

In Wolkenstein's monophonic songs, the notations used suggest both measured and unmeasured types of rhythm. Koller suggests that even in the measured songs there is a certain freedom in the relationship between long and short syllables.[7] This is supported by the fact that some of the songs which exist in two manuscripts are written in even notes (suggesting duple rhythm) in one manuscript and a clearly triple rhythm in the other. "Zergangen ist meins herzen we," here shown in the duple version, might actually have been sung from this manuscript with some inequality in the length of the syllables, without necessarily binding the singer to a strict duple *or* triple time. The version in the Vienna manuscript, however, employs the clear signs of polyphonic notation to show triple time, and even uses a short section with the red notes indicating hemiola rhythm (three notes in the time of two), which is a precisely defined rhythmic relationship.

It is interesting to note that the solmization syllables the text describes the birds as singing do *not* correspond to the notes of the melody.

[7]Oswald Koller, *Oswald von Wolkenstein. Geistliche und weltliche Lieder, Denkmäler der Tonkunst in Österreich*, IX[1] (Vienna, Artaria, 1902), 133.

"Nu huss!" sprach der Michel von Wolkenstain

"Nu huss!" sprach der Mi - chel von Wol - ken - stain, "so he-tzen wir!" sprach

Os - walt von Wol - ken - stain, "Za hürs!" sprach her Lien-hart von Wol - ken -

stain, "si mües-sen al - le flie - hen von Greif-fen-stain ge - leich."

Innsbruck, Universitätsbibliothek, f. 36.

"Attack!" Spoke Sir Michael von Wolkenstein
("Nu huss!" sprach der Michel von Wolkenstain)

In the year 1418 Duke Friedrich II of Austria was placed under the ban of the empire and, as a result, the nobility of the Tyrol area rebelled against him. These are the first three stanzas of a victory song which tells of the successful defense of Greifenstein Castle against the troops of the duke. The word "loan" in the third stanza also means a granting of a fief in Middle High German, so that the line has a double meaning, the second being that the singer is renouncing his feudal obligations to Friedrich. The lack of consistency of metrical structure which one sees in the stanzas is not infrequent with Wolkenstein.

"Attack!" spoke Sir Michael von Wolkenstein;
"Let's get them!" spoke Oswald von Wolkenstein;
"Let fly!" spoke Sir Leonard von Wolkenstein,
"from Greifenstein we'll send them quickly on their
  way."

And then a rain of fire began to fall
down on the heads beneath the castle wall

and burned on armor, helmets, bows and all;
they left these as they ran, which caused us no
  dismay.

Their heavy weapons, tents, and fire shield
were burned to ashes in the upper field;
I hear an evil loan will evil yield
and thus we're glad to give Duke Friedrich all his
  pay.

Many of Wolkenstein's songs are influenced by folk song, as is this vigorous little tune. The dactylic rhythms of the text are clearly notated in semibreves and minims, giving a brisk and forthright quality to the song.

Oh Tell Me, Love, What Does It Mean
(Sag an, herzlieb, nu was bedeutet)

A man, a woman, and the watchman's horn sing this dawn song. The first two lines of the first two stanzas are sung by the woman, the final lines of the first two stanzas and the entire third stanza are sung by the horn. All three

Sag an, herzlieb, nu was bedeutet

hard, am-sel droschel, der vink und ain zei-se-lein, das nen-net sich gug-guk.

hab ur-laub, höchster schatz, kurz-lich her-wi-der-ruck.

Innsbruck, Universitätsbibliothek, f. 17.
Transcription based on Oswald Koller, *Oswald von Wolkenstein. Geistliche und weltliche Lieder, Denkmäler der Tonkunst in Österreich*, IX[1] (Vienna, Artaria, 1902), 196.

of these stanzas are in the discantus. The last three stanzas are sung by the man and are in the tenor. The song thus presents a series of duets in counterpoint, sung by the woman and the man and the horn and the man. It will be noted that the same rhymes appear in the first and fourth stanzas, the second and fifth stanzas, and the third and sixth stanzas. However, since these pairs of stanzas make up duets, the rhyme words actually come very close together.

"Oh tell me, love, what does it mean for us, this
    loud and frightening hail,
these tones that swell?"
"Aa-hoo, get up, your nakedness conceal."

"My own, why should this stranger come and cause
    us sadly to lament
your leaving me?"
"Aa-hoo, aa-hoo, soon now the sun will shine.

"Be on your way,   though you would stay,
hear, hear, this morn,   the sounding horn!
Quick, up!   Jump up!   Hurry up!
The birds are singing in the wood: the blackbird,
    thrush, the finch
and a bird that calls itself cuckoo."

"Now, lady, hear the horn's sad wail;
hill and dale,   every vale   tells its tale,

and I hear the nightingale.
The crimson of the morning rises from the blue;
    blow well,
oh watchman, your vexation I can feel.

"A wind blows from the orient,
unspent,   it lights the firmament
and turns our joy to discontent.
My tender, loving maiden, the horn now thunders
    angrily.
I hear you, horn.   You grieve this maid of mine.

"Away, away, away, away!
Longing dismay,   murderous day,
our pain cannot withstand you any more.
Goodbye, my dearest love, I'll soon come back to
    you."

One of the most important polyphonic forms of the French medieval period was the polytextual motet, in which each part added above the tenor had an independent text. This polytextual technique continued into the fourteenth cenutry, and was used by Wolkenstein for one of his polyphonic songs, "Sag an, herzlieb." The song is also marked by frequent use of figures imitating the sound of the watchman's horn, and occasionally even by imitation between the parts, as at the beginning of the *Abgesang*.

The May with Blossoms Frail
(*Der may mit lieber zal*)

In this song Oswald von Wolkenstein imitates the sounds of nature with a virtuosity unexcelled even in his baroque age. The effect of such sound imitation is heightened by a brilliant display of rhyme in which the emphasis is also on sound rather than meaning. In a work such as this, poetic qualities are almost completely subordinated to musical qualities.

The May with blossoms frail
has decked the earth to good avail,
mountain, meadow, hill, and dale.
The birds rehearse each scale,
with ringing   and singing   loudly hail
the finch and thrush, the lark and nightingale.
The angry cuckoo sped
with beating wings outspread
after little birds, who fled.
This is what he said:
"Cuckoo, cuckoo, cuckoo,
give me my due,
that will I have from you.
My hunger   makes me younger,
quicker to pursue."
"Beware!   Oh where
to flee?   So cried the chickadee.
Goldfinch, titmouse, thrush, now come and sing:
"sa and too-ee too-ee too-ee too-ee
sa sa sa sa sa sa sa sa sa sa sa
fi fideli fideli fideli fi,
ci cieriri ci ci cieriri,
ci ri ciwigg cidiwigg fici fici."
Thus sang the cuckoo: "Kawa wa coo coo."

"Raco," the raven spoke,
"My voice, too, is sweet,
wheat   I adore,
this song outpour:
'Give more!   Encore!   I implore!'"
"Liri liri liri liri liri liri lon,"

thus sang the lark,   thus sang the lark,   thus
   sang the lark.
"I sing of a woodthrush,   I sing of a woodthrush,
   I sing of a woodthrush,"
comes ringing from the forest.
"You court,   disport,
harry,   are merry,
here and there,
just as does our pastor
Cidiwigg cidiwigg cidiwigg,
cificigo cificigo cificigo nightingale,
whose singing rivals the beauty of the grail."

"Neigh neigh neigh," cried out the colt,
"let us all sing too!"
"Moo," the cows say,
the donkeys bray:
"Put the sack upon my back!"
"Heehaw heehaw heehaw heehaw heehaw heehaw
   come,"
so cried the mule,   so cried the mule,   so cried
   the mule.
"Be silent!" said the miller's wife,
"Get up!" spoke the farmer's wife,
"Move along for all your life,
bray if you will, I say, but walk,
don't balk,   or else the hawk
will tear your hide with many a squawk!
Go on, go on, go on, go on!
Off with harness!
Get along, Walburg!
Stir yourself as you should,
Weidmann, and run and graze within the wood."

Thirty-one of Wolkenstein's songs are polyphonic compositions which really mark the beginning of the German polyphonic *Lied*. They vary in style from note-against-note syllabic settings of a text to canonic songs showing the influence of contemporary French contrapuntal techniques.

The texts include everything from dawn songs to a Latin hymn. Most of the songs are for two voices, although

Der may mit lieber zal

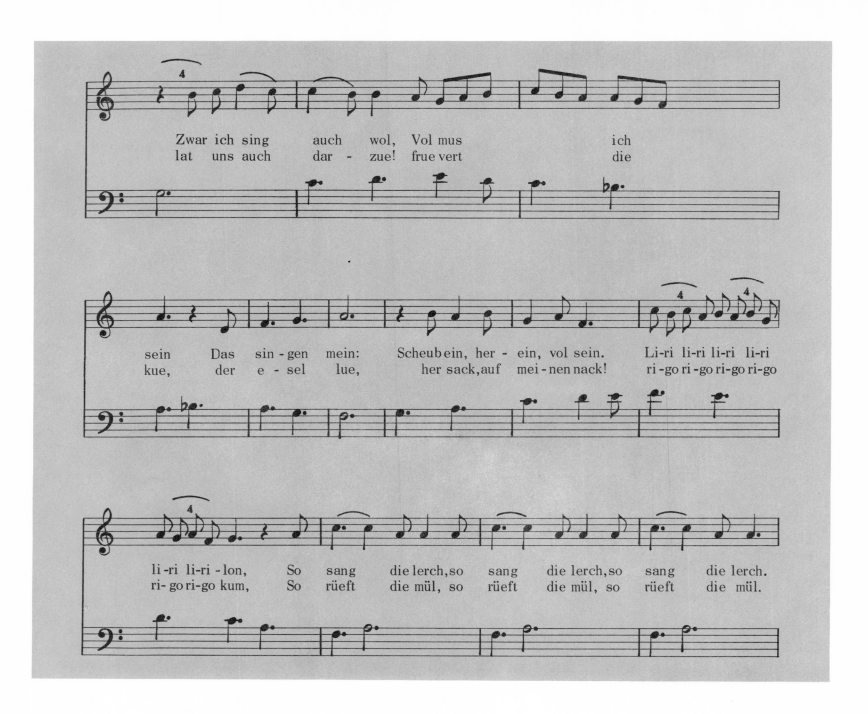

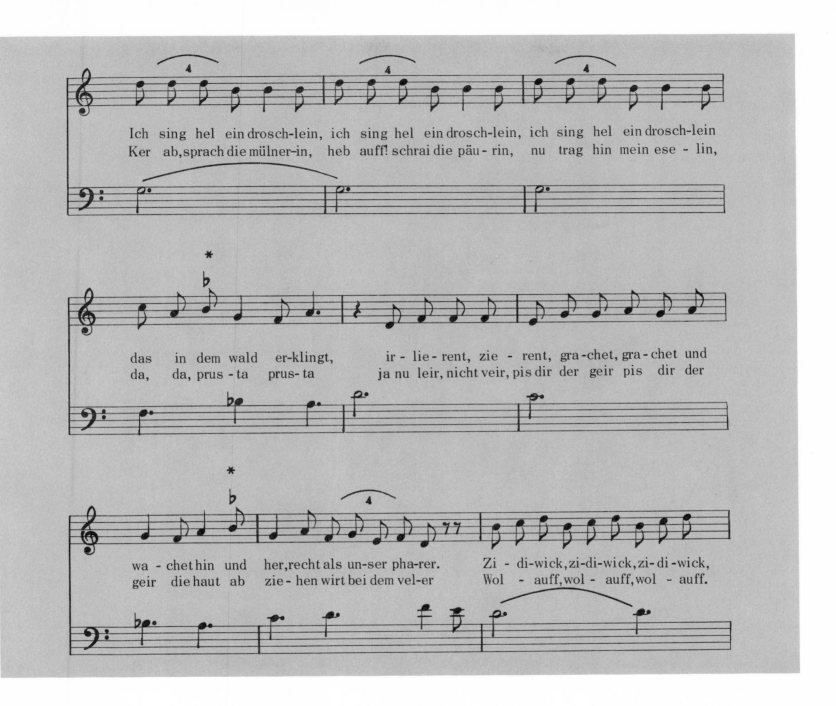

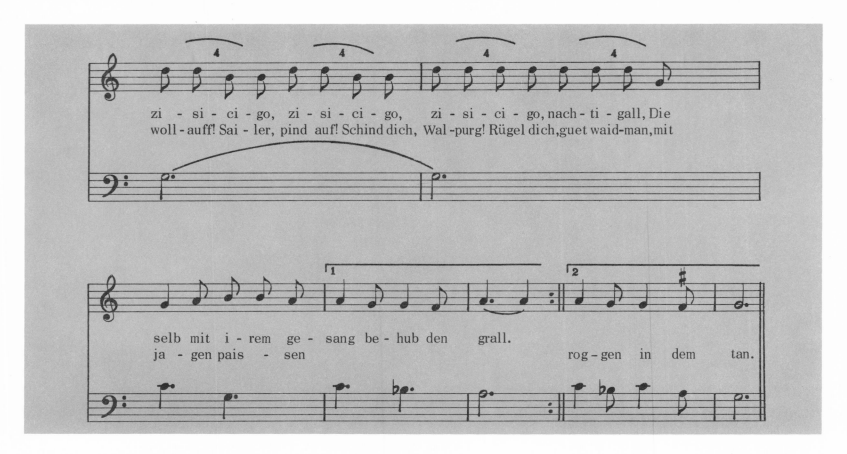

Vienna, Nationalbibliothek, Hs. 2777, f. 19.

Transcription from Archibald Davison and Willi Apel, *Historical Anthology of Music* (Cambridge, Harvard University Press, 1949), p. 64. (The text of the third stanza is omitted in Davison and Apel.)

*These flats are supplied by the compiler of this anthology.

there are several examples of three-part songs and even a few in four parts. The most famous of the polyphonic pieces, "Der may mit lieber zal," is actually an arrangement in two parts of a three-part *virelai* by the French composer Vaillant. It is full of delightful imitations of bird songs, the text-painting of which the French were later so fond and of which examples are also to be found in the songs of the Monk of Salzburg and Wizlaw.

Index of Songs

Index of Names

The Songs of the Minnesingers

FRIEDRICH VON HAUSEN
Mir ist daz herze wunt

Friedrich von Hausen was a twelfth-century Rhinelander in the court of Friedrich I (Barbarossa). His poetry is strongly influenced by the courtly love songs of the troubadours and trouvères, and it is probable that he borrowed some of their melodies for his songs. The tune for this song is a contrafact of an anonymous trouvère song, "Mult m'a demoré."

HEINRICH VON VELDEKE
Ich bin vrô, sint ons die dage

In German poetry, the cult of minne (courtly love) really begins with Veldeke. The song given here is one of the few minnesongs expressing the lady's feelings. The melodies for all Veldeke's poems have been lost, but it is believed that, like Hausen, he borrowed freely from Romance sources. This melody is a contrafact of "Fine amour et bone esperance" (probably by Gace Brulé).

WOLFRAM VON ESCHENBACH
Jamer ist mir entsprungen

Wolfram von Eschenbach belongs to the classical period of the minnesong and was a contemporary of Walther von der Vogelweide. Though best known today for his epic poetry (particularly *Parzival*), in his own time he was also renowned for his minnesongs. "Jamer ist mir entsprungen" is a lyric stanza from *Titurel,* an Arthurian romance which may have been intended as an interlude for *Parzival.* The melody fits all the stanzas of *Titurel* and is one of the few surviving examples of music for epic poetry. In this stanza, Sigune, the heroine, sings sorrowingly of her longing for her lover, Schianatulander.

WALTHER VON DER VOGELWEIDE
Nu alrêst leb' ich mir werde

In the poetry of Walther von der Vogelweide the minnesong reaches its greatest perfection. In his crusade song, he speaks of his feelings on arriving in the Holy Land. This song is the only one for which Walther's melody has survived in its entirety.

Mir hat her Gerhart Atze ein pfert erschozzen

Not all the songs of the minnesingers were serious. In this song, Walther relates an incident which may actually have occurred, in which one Sir Gerhart Atze shot the poet's horse. The tune is an adaptation of one of the songs ascribed to Walther in Adam Puschman's songbook, a collection of meistersinger melodies.

Uns hat der winter geschat über al

The dactylic rhythm of this song indicates that it is from Walther's early period, during which he was strongly influenced by Romance song. The tune is a contrafact of "Quant voi les prés flourir et blanchoier" by Moniot d'Arras (possibly Moniot de Paris).

NEIDHART VON REUENTHAL
Kint, bereitet iuch der sliten ûf daz îs!

Neidhart introduced a new realistic element into the minnesong. His songs describe village events and the charms of peasant girls, often in a mocking bitter vein. His songs are divided into two groups, summer songs and winter songs. This song begins with a typical "nature stanza" describing winter and in subsequent stanzas relates events at a village dance. The melodies of more of Neidhart's songs have been preserved than those of any other minnesinger. His tunes are characteristically vigorous and robust dance melodies.

Blôzen wir den anger ligen sâhen

Neidhart begins with a description of the coming of spring. Later stanzas present an argument between a peasant girl, who is enamored of the knightly poet, and her more realistic and practical mother. This song is one of the very few in which the rhythm is shown in the notation in the original manuscript.

Sinc an, guldîn huon! ich gibe dir weize

This sprightly tune is from the Neidhart fragment in the Staatsbibliothek at Frankfort-am-Main; another version is found in the larger Berlin collection of Neidhart's songs. The poet sings of the pretty maid who entices him and then dashes his hopes. This stanza is followed by a description of a lusty dance at the village inn.

DER UNVERZAGTE
Der kuninc rodolp mynnet got

The later thirteenth-century minnesingers included much didactic verse among their writings. The form of the *Spruch* (a single stanza treating subjects other than courtly love) was extensively cultivated. Such poems make up the bulk of the works of this poet, who wrote under the pseudonym Der Unverzagte. In the *Spruch* sung here, the many virtues of King Rudolph I (founder of the Hapsburg dynasty in Austria) are listed, but the poet concludes with an unexpected twist—the king, he says, likes to hear the minnesingers perform but forgets to pay them!

HERMANN DAMEN
Eyn lob syng ich dir tzu prise

Hermann Damen is one of the increasing number of middle-class minnesingers of the later thirteenth century. Most of his verse is didactic or religious, with much clever and artful manipulation of rhyme and form. This is quite evident in his hymn of praise to the Triune God.

FRAUENLOB (HEINRICH VON MEISSEN)
Ey ich sach in dem trone

Frauenlob is the best known of the later minnesingers. Among his many works are examples of the long sectional form called the *Leich* (lay). His most famous one is *The Lay of Our Lady,* in which he has twenty-two stanzas of varying structures dealing with the Virgin Mary. Only the first two are given here.

WIZLAW VON RÜGEN
Ic parrêre dî dorch mîne trôwe

Wizlaw, the ruler of the Baltic island of Rügen, was among the last of the minnesingers. His songs often show a return to the spirit of the classical minnesong. This song, a warm and personal love song, was possibly written for his wife.

HUGO VON MONTFORT
Fro welt ir sint gar hüpsch und schön

Though some of the minnesingers probably used tunes written by others, Montfort is the only one to acknowledge the composer of his tunes, Burk Mangolt. In the dialogue song given here Montfort speaks of renouncing the world, and Dame World attempts to dissuade him. The song was written at the time of the death of his second wife.

Ich fröw mich gen des abentz kunft

In this traditional dawn song, the singer describes his longing for the coming of his beloved at evening, and his sweet distress at the coming of dawn and the time of parting. Like many of Montfort's songs, the melody contains several long textless phrases which may have been performed by an instrument.

OSWALD VON WOLKENSTEIN
Der may mit lieber zal

Oswald von Wolkenstein comes at the end of the period of the German minnesong. His work includes monophonic songs in the old tradition, some poems which point in the direction of the more mechanical productions of the meistersingers, and many polyphonic compositions which lead to the German polyphonic *Lied.* In "Der may mit lieber zal" the poet imitates the sounds of nature with evident delight. The instrumental part is provided by the composer.

NOTES ON THE PERFORMANCE

Though all indications are that minnesongs were sung with instrumental accompaniment by a variety of instruments, no specific instructions to the instrumentalist have survived, except in a very few late songs. Accordingly, instrumental parts have been constructed, using what appear to have been the most popular types of instruments: lute, recorder, and a bowed stringed instrument.

PERFORMERS

JERRY DAVIDSON, *tenor*
ELIZABETH HOWICK, *soprano*
BARBARA SEAGRAVE, *lute and percussion*
ALLAN GOVE, *viol*
ROGER WIDDER, *recorder*

Mr. Davidson and Mrs. Howick are graduates in Music at the University of Arkansas; Dr. Seagrave, Mr. Gove, and Mr. Widder are members of the faculty of the Department of Music of the University of Arkansas.

J. PHILLIP EAGLE, *sound engineer*